What Do I Like To Do?

101 Activities To Identify
Interests and Plan Careers

Janet E. Wall

pro·ed
An International Publisher

8700 Shoal Creek Boulevard
Austin, TX 78757-6897
800/897-3202   Fax 800/397-7633
www.proedinc.com

© 2005 by PRO-ED, Inc.
8700 Shoal Creek Boulevard
Austin, Texas 78757-6897
800/897-3202   Fax 800/397-7633
www.proedinc.com

ISBN 1-4164-0049-4

This book was developed by Innerchoice
Publishing and Jalmar Press, in cooperation
with the publisher, PRO-ED, Inc.

Printed in the United States of America

2   3   4   5   6   7   8   9   10   08

Acknowledgments

I would like to acknowledge the following individuals who have provided ideas, assistance, and support in the creation of this book.

Initial advice about the need, scope, and feasibility of this book was supplied by former colleagues John Stine, Terri Lonowski, and Sylvia Bourn. Their encouragement helped create the necessary enthusiasm to drive the completion of this book. Counsel, support, and advice from them on this and other endeavors is frequently sought, freely delivered, and always appreciated. Beyond her moral support, Terri compiled a review of one of the interest inventories that is included in this book. All three were important in the creation of this document.

Special appreciation is extended to Dr. Rebecca Dedmond, Director of School Counseling who, along with her graduate students at George Washington University, provided assistance in gathering necessary information to complete this book, as well as refining various parts to make it more appropriate for its intended audience. Thanks are also extended to Susan Scharf for her help on reviewing one of the interest inventories and to her middle and high school students who provided input for some of the activities in this book.

Recognition is extended to the U.S. Army for its support of Planning for Life activities and the development, with input from Nancy Perry and Dr. Pat Schwallie-Giddis working with the American School Counselor Association, of the public domain basic career plan used in Chapter 2 of this book. I borrowed extensively from their ideas for the Career Planning section of this book.

Finally, I would like to thank my husband, Dr. Robert Gard, for his unqualified support of my activities. He has always been willing, generally gleefully, to review my writing to see if it makes sense and communicates to the audience. I'm glad he is my partner in life.

Table of Contents

Chapter 3: Selecting and Using the Right Inventory for Your Students and Clients

Introduction

Our interests drive and dictate many of our decisions. We select our careers, our activities, our hobbies, and sometimes our friends based on what we like. This book focuses on our interests and how they permeate our lives in so many ways. It provides opportunities for individuals to begin to understand how their interests relate to various aspects of their lives so that they can make the best decision in all life choices including educational and career pursuits.

Career counselors, school counselors, workforce development professionals and others can benefit from this book as they work with students or clients in groups or in individual counseling settings.

The book has four chapters:

Chapter 1: This introductory chapter reviews the general topic of interests and the theory behind why they are considered important in how our interests relate to our environment. This chapter focuses on the Holland Vocational PersonalityTheory and the six categories of personality or interests that it measures. The Holland theory was selected because it is the most widely used and most easily understood framework for discussing one's interests. Emphasis is given to the notion that most people have interests in all six areas with some areas more dominant or stronger than others. Further, we seek environments such as careers, hobbies, etc., based on our interest areas.

Chapter 2: This chapter contains 101 activities that can be used with individuals from elementary school students through adults. These activities are organized into six categories including:

- Measuring Interests
- School Subjects Activities
- Out of School Activities
- Education and Training Activities
- Occupations and Jobs Activities
- Career Planning

The purpose of this chapter is to help individuals better understand their interests and see how their interests permeate their life choices from the courses that they select, the careers they pursue, and the leisure activities in which they participate.

Clearly you will not use all of the activities with each student or client, but a large selection is provided in each category so that you may choose the activity most appropriate for the student you are working with. You will find it useful to engage each student in as many of these activities as possible so that you provide a strong foundation of understanding upon which your students can make their life decisions. Hopefully, these activities will also inspire you to create new activities that will help your students in exploring their particular interests.

Chapter 3: In order to work with the activities in Chapter 2, students or clients need to first identify their interest areas. This can be done quickly and cheaply by using the short checklists provided in Chapter 2 in the Measuring Interests section. These short instruments can provide an overview of one's interests if a published instrument is not readily available.

It is best, though, for you to use one of the published interest inventories created by professional test makers. They have used professionally acceptable procedures and considerable resources to create high quality instruments that have been tested and researched with applicable populations. They are committed to upholding certain testing standards, and as a result, they provide proven instruments that are supported to one extent or another by research studies.

Because there are so many interest inventories from which to select, it is important to know how to pick an inventory that meets your needs and those of the students or clients who will be taking them. This chapter outlines and explains several criteria that are important to consider in selecting the right assessment tool. These criteria include considerations of technical strength, relevance, and utility. The chapter closes with a checklist that you can use to help you judge the quality and applicability of the instrument for your particular use.

Chapter 4: There are several published inventories that can be used to measure interests. General information about the instruments that purport to measure the interest areas associated with the Holland Vocational Personality Theory have been collected from the publishers and included in this section. Information on the reliability, validity, support materials, and plans for the future are included for each of the inventories.

Appendix A: This section contains a listing of occupations by interest area as developed by the U.S. Department of Labor. This listing is used in a number of activities included in Chapter 2.

Appendix B: A great deal of helpful information on interests can be accessed over the Internet. Some information is useful and credible and some is not. Several web sites that are of particular quality and utility are highlighted in this chapter. These web sites contain high quality information that can help counselors, teachers, and parents augment career and personal development activities conducted in schools, and help adults with their career progression and job hunting.

Ten Ways This Book Can Help You

You should use the information in this book in a flexible fashion to meet your particular needs and the needs of your students or clients. There are many ways to extract information from this book to augment your career exploration and career development programs. Some major ways you can use the contents of this book include:

1. Select a Published Interest Inventory for Your Program
2. Get a Quick Idea of Student Interests Without Using a Published Inventory
3. Learn Why Interests Are Important to Our Current and Future Actions and Decisions
4. Help Students Understand How Their Interests Relate to School Subjects
5. Work with Teachers to Integrate the Concept of Interests Into the School Curriculum
6. Help Students See That Interests Affect Their Personal Lives and Actions
7. Connect Students' or Clients' Interests to Education and Training Activities
8. Involve Local Employers in Your Career Development Program
9. Help Students Plan Careers
10. Find Additional Resources

Using the examples that follow, you can use various parts of this book to meet your personal objectives.

Example 1

Task	Steps/Method
Select a Published Interest Inventory for Your Program	• Read the contents of Chapter 3 to determine what characteristics are important in selecting an interest inventory for your students or clients. • Read the basic information provided on several interest inventories in Chapter 4, and select one or more for further investigation. • Request a sample set from the publishers. • Review the instruments and the manuals and complete the checklist provided for you in this book. • Select the inventory that is best for your situation and administer it to your students or clients. • Discuss the results with your students or clients.

Example 2

Task	Steps/Method
Get a Quick Idea of Student Interests Without Using a Published Inventory	• Using the Measuring Interests section of Chapter 2, make multiple copies of one or more of these checklists (or use the free computer versions) and have your students or clients complete the inventories. • Review the results with your students or clients. • Discuss the meanings of the interest areas that are measured. • Ask the students if the results seem to fit them.

Example 3

Task	Steps/Method
Learn Why Interests Are Important to Our Current and Future Actions and Decisions	• Using Chapter 1, read the information on why interests are important to our experiences and decisions. • Develop a solid understanding of the interest areas in the Holland Vocational Personality Theory. • Determine why interests are important in the selection of occupations and future training and education.

Example 4

Task	Steps/Method
Help Students Understand How Their Interests Relate to School Subjects	• Using the School Subjects section of Chapter 2, select a few relevant activities that will help tie together students' interests to what they are experiencing in school. • Depending upon your time constraints, assign a few activities for class time and/or a few for homework. • Discuss the results with your students to help clarify their understandings and help them make connections between their interests and their time in school.

Example 5

Task	Steps/Method
Work with Teachers to Integrate the Concept of Interests into the School Curriculum	• Using the School Subjects section of Chapter 2, select activities that can be conducted by teachers of various school subjects or in cooperation with them. • There are activities that relate to various skills in mathematics, English, reading, social studies, art, science, etc. • Review the activities with your colleagues. • Arrange to have subject area teachers conduct some of the activities or supplement them in some way. • Discuss how the results of these activities relate to what students know about their own interest areas either from the checklists or from a published interest inventory.

Example 6

Task	Steps/Method
Help Students See That Interests Affect Their Personal Lives and Actions	• Using the Out of School Activities section of Chapter 2, you can select one or more activities that ask students to relate interests to various non-school and non-occupational areas such as hobbies and other leisure activities. • Administer one or more activities that seem appropriate. These can be assigned as homework, if you desire. • Discuss with your students or clients how their interests have developed through various out of school activities. • Have students discuss with you and with each other how their own interests tend to dictate what they do during their leisure time.

Example 7

Task	Steps/Method
Connect Students' or Clients' Interests to Education and Training Activities	• Using the section on Education and Training activities in Chapter 2, you will find many opportunities to show students how education and training relate to interests. • When it is part of your program to start discussing post-high school goals, have the students or clients use some of the activities that help to show how interests relate to post-secondary courses, programs, and majors. • Be sure to help your students or clients understand how their interests reflect their future educational choices.

Example 8

Task	Steps/Method
Involve Local Employers in Your Career Development Program	• Involving local employers is important for your career development program. Chapter 2 provides some activities that help students or clients link their interests to what happens in the workforce. • After selecting relevant activities, contact local employers to gain their support for and involvement with relevant activities. • Help arrange for students to visit applicable local businesses or organizations as needed. • Have the students complete the activities that you have chosen. • Discuss with the students or your clients how their interests and the interests of employees are the same or different. • Discuss with your students or clients how it takes a variety of types of people with differing interests to make a company work smoothly and well.

Example 9

Task	Steps/Method
Help Students Plan Careers	• Using the section on Career Planning in Chapter 2, use the example career plans as an organizer to help students develop a framework for thinking about and organizing information about themselves and how that relates to occupations and educational plans. Example plans are provided for students at the elementary, middle, high school, and post-secondary school levels. • Use this plan with your students or clients to help them plot out their current situation and their future goals and activities. • Discuss with them how their interests are influencing their career plans.

Example 10

Task	Steps/Method
Find Additional Resources	• Using Appendix B, learn about the various career development and occupational web sites that are available to assist you and your students or clients. • Review these sites to see what you and your students can gain from them. These web sites provide solid and competent information to help you develop your career development program. • Use the information in these web sites to augment your career center resources.

A Typical Path

In order to help students or clients identify and use their interests in selecting courses, hobbies, education and training programs, and occupations, you need to help them identify their interest areas. Thus, it is important to provide some mechanism to help them do so. This can be done by administering the checklists or inventories provided in the Measuring Interests section of Chapter 2, and/or through one of the many published inventories listed in Chapter 4. Helping students interpret this information is crucial to their self-understanding. Therefore, it is incumbent upon you to discuss their results with them so that they may internalize the information.

Once interest areas are identified, you can help students see the relationship between their interests and their school subjects, hobbies, friends, educational programs, training programs, the workplace, and occupational choices. This is accomplished through the rest of the activities in Chapter 2. Using this information, you will be able to assist individuals in using knowledge of their interests in planning for their future.

You can use the following steps as a way of organizing the process you will take your students or clients through.

- **Recognize** Interest Areas
- **Internalize** Results
- **Personalize** Knowledge
- **Externalize** Information
- **Strategize** for the Future

The chart below suggests a basic path you might take to show the connection of interests to everyday life and future decision-making. Depending on the age and needs of your students or clients, you may follow the entire path from identifying one's interests to planning for careers, or you may wish to concentrate on portions of the process, such as helping elementary or middle school students understand how school subjects and hobbies are related to their interests.

Steps to Understanding and Using Interests for Career Planning

Steps	Process
Recognize Interest Areas	• Use Checklists or Published Interest Inventories
Internalize Results	• Discuss Results with Students or Clients • Help Individuals in the Understanding of the RIASEC Areas
Personalize Knowledge	• Identify How Interest Areas Relate to School Subjects, Majors, Hobbies, and Other Activities

Externalize Information	• Show the Relationship of Interests to Further Education and Training • Show How Interests Relate to Occupational Choices • Show How Interests Relate to Their Future Income, Job Prospects, Life Styles, Training Requirements, etc.
Strategize for the Future	• Use Knowledge About Their Interests to Plan Their Next Steps (middle school to high school; high school to post-secondary education training programs, jobs; transition from education and training programs to occupations and jobs)

The ways you use this book will be determined by the individuals with whom you work, their needs and developmental levels, and your career development and career planning programs. Your use will be limited only by your creativity and motivation to assist others in their life journeys.

Chapter 1:

Understanding Interests and Why
They Are Important

Career development professionals generally believe that abilities or aptitudes, interests, and values are critical concepts as individuals evolve in their thinking about the selection of daily life choices, careers, and life planning activities. An individual's abilities, interests, and values can be matched to an environment's ability requirements, its opportunity to satisfy one's interests, and its ability to fulfill one's values. In the world of career development models, this is called Person-Environment Fit.

The greater the match or fit between the characteristics of the person and the characteristics of the environment, the more satisfied and productive the person is likely to be. This person-environment fit concept applies to an individual's choice of work, school subjects, leisure activities, hobbies, and general preferences. In the world of work, when there is a high degree of match between the characteristics of the individual and the requirements and characteristics of an occupation, there is an optimal career fit. This notion is illustrated in the graphic below.

Person-Environment Fit
Optimal Match

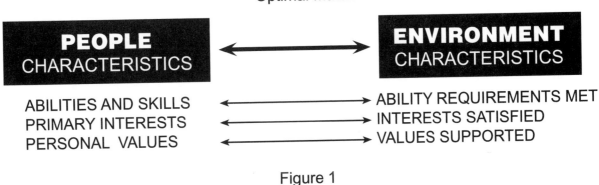

PEOPLE CHARACTERISTICS		ENVIRONMENT CHARACTERISTICS
ABILITIES AND SKILLS	⟷	ABILITY REQUIREMENTS MET
PRIMARY INTERESTS	⟷	INTERESTS SATISFIED
PERSONAL VALUES	⟷	VALUES SUPPORTED

Figure 1

This book deals primarily with the **interests** part of this model and how interests relate to occupations, school subjects, hobbies, and other leisure activities. More than 100 activities have been provided for you to integrate the notion of interests into your educational and career development program.

Several researchers and career development professionals espouse the person-environment fit model. We, however, are focusing on the Holland Personality Theory in this book because of the ease with which counselors, students, and clients can grasp the basic concepts and use them easily and effectively in career development and life planning activities.

The Role of Interests in Career Development

According to many theorists and researchers, occupational and life choices are based on personal behavioral style or personality. Interests are expressions of that personality, and thus play a key role in the process of career development.

Holland (1997) presented the following principles or themes related to personality and occupational choice:

- The choice of an occupation is an expression of personality (p. 7).

- Interest inventories are inventories of personality (p. 8).

- The members of an occupational group have similar personalities and similar histories of personal development (p. 10).

- Because people in an occupational group have similar personalities, they will respond to many situations and problems in similar ways (p. 11).

- Occupational achievement, stability, and satisfaction depend on degree of similarity between one's personality and the job environment (pgs. 7-11).

In refining his theory, Holland proposed four assumptions:

- People can be categorized as one of six categories or types: realistic, investigative, artistic, social, enterprising, or conventional (p. 3).

- Environments can be categorized in the same six types: realistic, investigative, artistic, social, enterprising, or conventional (p. 3).

- People search for environments that allow them to exhibit and use their skills and abilities, express their attitudes and values, and take on agreeable problems and roles (p. 4).

- Persons behave as determined by an interaction between their personality and the characteristics of the environment (pgs. 2-4).

The RIASEC Areas

Holland's six areas — realistic, investigative, artistic, social, enterprising, and conventional — are handy because they are used to describe both people and the environment. The six areas are fairly easy to understand, serve as useful labels for description and conversation, and provide a common language for career development professionals and the people they serve.

Holland (1997) specified that people can be described in the six categories by the following characteristics:

Realistic (R). People in this category have a preference for the use of tools, working with their hands, working with animals, and working with objects and materials. Activities tend to be concrete and practical. Example occupations include instrument repairers, surveyors, mechanics, carpenters, airline pilots, and jewelers. Descriptors of **Realistic** people include frank, genuine, persistent, thrifty, conforming, materialistic, practical, natural, and asocial.

Investigative (I). Persons in this category have a preference for analytical work that involves observations, symbols, systematic problem solving, troubleshooting and the creation and use of knowledge. Example occupations include scientists, researchers, statisticians, surgeons, pharmacists, and market research analysts. Descriptors of **Investigative** people would include analytical, critical, complex, curious, intellectual, precise, rational, and reserved.

Artistic (A). People in this category enjoy creative work in the areas of music, writing, dance, performance, and art. They prefer to be in environments where they are free from systematized and ordered activities. Free expression is important. Example occupations include models, floral arrangers, dancers, sculptors, and musicians. Descriptors of **Artistic** people include complicated, emotional, expressive, idealistic, imaginative, impulsive, nonconforming, and sensitive.

Social (S). Persons in this group prefer working with and for people in a helpful and assistive way. They like to be involved in informing, teaching, training, solving personal problems for others, and curing people. Example occupations include nurses, physical therapists, teachers, clergy, and security guards. Descriptors of **Social** people would include cooperative, friendly, generous, helpful, idealistic, kind, sociable, and warm.

Enterprising (E). People in this category like to work with people in a persuasive way. They like to lead people, take risks for economic gain, sell, and achieve organizational goals. Example occupations include telemarketers, managers, program directors, sales representatives, coaches, and travel agents and guides. Descriptors of **Enterprising** people would include adventurous, ambitious, domineering, energetic, extroverted, self-confident, and talkative.

Conventional (C). Persons in this category prefer activities that are ordered with systematic rules and procedures. They like record keeping, filing materials, and organizing things into categories according to a plan. Example occupations include economists, tax preparers, librarians, accountants, and budget analysts. Descriptors of **Conventional** people would include careful, conforming, conscientious, efficient, inflexible, methodical, obedient, and thrifty (Holland, 1997, pgs. 23-28).

The Holland Vocational Personality Theory contends that the environments, like occupations, leisure activities, and selection of courses and training programs can be described according to the same six areas. These environments tend to reinforce and reward the behaviors of people of similar type.

RIASEC Codes

For ease of use of Holland's system, we often refer to the shorthand of **RIASEC** (REE- A – SEC) codes when discussing the characteristics of a person, occupation, or activity. The term **RIASEC** is derived from the first letter of each of the interest areas of **R**ealistic, **I**nvestigative, **A**rtistic, **S**ocial, **E**nterprising, and **C**onventional.

Generally, occupations, hobbies, leisure activities, and other life choices are best described by more than one interest area. For example, the occupation geologist can satisfy an interest of a person who is **Investigative (I)** because geologists collect and interpret information in order to solve a problem. Geologists also like to be in the field collecting data, working with their hands, and using equipment. That would show that a geologist is also **Realistic (R)** in nature. A similar situation would occur for a science teacher who wants to help people **(S)**, but enjoys problem solving and the scientific method **(I)**.

The same is true for all people, as we do not fit nicely into one and only one category. In reality we tend to be a combination of all six interests; some interest areas are just stronger than others.

Although general practice is to use two or three interest codes to describe people and environments, it is important to note that throughout this book, for purposes of simplicity, we refer to the primary interest area or primary interest code of an individual, a hobby, an education program, or an occupation. That is, we use only one interest area to label these areas.

The activities in Chapter 2 generally call for the use of one interest area, but you could modify the activities to use two or three interest areas, if you feel it necessary, useful, or practical to do so. Young people may easily be confused by using multiple **RIASEC** descriptors, but individuals who have an understanding of occupations and life planning may find this additional complexity to be more appropriate and accurate. You, as the counselor or facilitator, should be able to make that judgment.

Basic Characteristics of the Holland Model

The Holland model is often displayed as a hexagon (See Figure 2), showing the relationship between each of the **RIASEC** areas. Based on data collected in research studies, it has been determined that the characteristics of people and occupations in categories that are adjacent are most similar. For example R and I and R and C are more similar than R and A or R and S or R and E. In fact, it is often stated that there is somewhat of an aversion to activities and occupations with characteristics in categories that are the opposite point of the hexagon. For example, Artistic people tend to have an aversion to activities and occupations in the Conventional category, and Investigative people tend to have an aversion to occupations and activities in the Enterprising category. For persons who have dominant interests in adjacent points, their profile is said to be consistent.

People and occupations do exist with these inconsistent codes, but according to the research, they are comparatively rare. I can attest to the existence of persons with inconsistent codes since I am a strong I and E, with S in second place. It certainly makes life interesting and challenging to work with these somewhat polar opposite codes that generally put me in a category very unlike my colleagues.

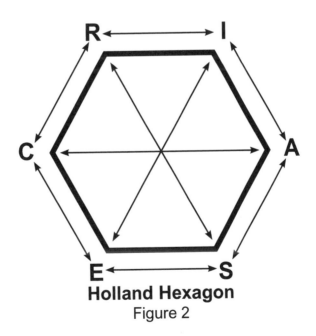

Holland Hexagon
Figure 2

From *Making Vocational Choices - A Theory of Vocational Personalities and Work Environments. 3e* (p. 6) by J.L. Holland, 1997, Odessa, FL: Psychological Assessment Resources, Inc. Adapted with Permission

The Holland Vocational Personality Theory is widely accepted as a useful mechanism for helping people understand themselves and for using that information to locate, and connect with, compatible activities and occupations. There are, however, three other concepts that are critical to the use of interests in career exploration and life planning. These are differentiation, congruence, and identity.

Differentiation. Differentiation refers to how well defined one's interests are. Most people have profiles that are defined or differentiated to some extent. That is, they may have a high interest in one, two, or three areas, and lower or less dominant interests in the other three areas. With a differentiated profile, it is easier to understand how the person's interests match up with other activities, occupations, and jobs.

An example is in Figure 3, where two areas are dominant and the other four are not. A person with this profile would probably find occupations and activities in which the **I** and **S** interests are associated to be compatible.

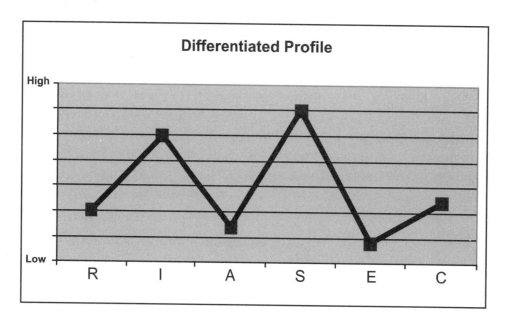

Figure 3

From *Making Vocational Choices - A Theory of Vocational Personalities and Work Environments. 3e* (p. 33) by J.L. Holland, 1997, Odessa, FL: Psychological Assessment Resources, Inc. Adapted with Permission

Undifferentiated profiles are more difficult to interpret and use. Some individuals may have high interests in all six areas or very low interests in all six areas. These types of profiles would be considered undifferentiated. Although this occurs on occasion, undifferentiated profiles are not particularly useful or helpful in career development. Individuals who have undifferentiated profiles may not have had sufficient life experiences to have developed stable or strong interests.

Undifferentiated High Profiles. It is quite possible that on interest measures or surveys, some individuals will indicate that they like or are interested in all the activities, occupations, and situations presented. Figure 4 shows an example of this type of profile.

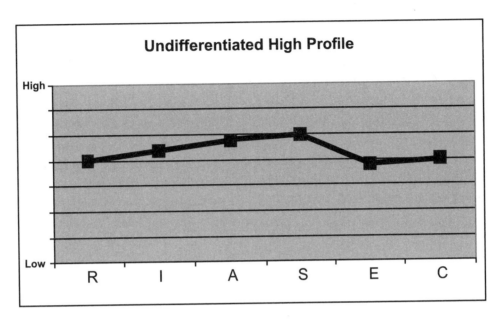

Figure 4
From *Making Vocational Choices - A Theory of Vocational Personalities and Work Environments. 3e* (p. 33) by J.L. Holland, 1997, Odessa, FL: Psychological Assessment Resources, Inc. Adapted with Permission

High, undifferentiated profiles may suggest the person is interested in just about everything. That situation would require further intervention and assistance from a counselor to determine verifications and explanations, and to identify priorities. This profile may change as the person gains experiences and begins to have preferences for some activities over others.

Low Undifferentiated Profiles. A low undifferentiated profile may suggest that a clinical intervention is appropriate. It may be the individual's mood, temperament, outlook on life, or lack of meaningful experiences contributed to the lack of interest in any area. It may well be that the individual is not sufficiently mature, or is too young, to have experienced enough of life to know what he or she prefers. An undifferentiated profile is represented by Figure 5.

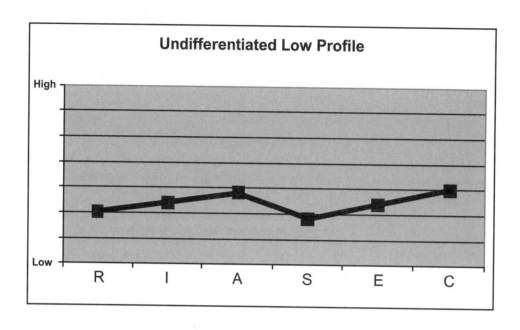

Figure 5

From *Making Vocational Choices - A Theory of Vocational Personalities and Work Environments. 3e* (p. 33)
by J.L. Holland, 1997, Odessa, FL: Psychological Assessment Resources, Inc. Adapted with Permission

Interests develop with time and experiences. Sometimes, very young individuals have not had a sufficient number of life experiences to really know what their interests are. In these cases, even well produced interest measures or surveys may not be very helpful. The best way to develop interests is to be exposed to a wide variety of experiences.

Congruence. For purposes of life and career planning, congruence may well be the most important concept. Congruence refers to the degree of match between the individual's interests and that of the activity, job, occupation, or plan of action. Congruence is high if the person is in a job or other activity that satisfies that person's interest area or areas. For example, a person who has a high interest area in the Realistic category and works in an environment that allows that interest to be expressed, experiences high congruence. If an Artistic person had to work in a Conventional occupation, the congruence would be low.

It has been shown that when congruence is high, job satisfaction, job performance, and longevity on the job are high. People are satisfied and happy when they are working in an environment that satisfies their interests.

Identity. Identity refers to how clear and stable one's goals, interest, and traits are. If a person is interested in many occupational goals, they do not have a clear identity.

The importance of interests in occupational and life planning is evident and it is important that students and clients understand their interests and how they relate to and influence choices that they make in life.

An important part of the Holland model is the need for self-knowledge and knowledge about occupations. Only then can good choices be made.

Along with abilities and values, interests are a very important part of knowledge of self and the knowledge of occupations and other environments. This book intends to help in the clarification of one's interests and to show how those interests relate to various aspects of one's life.

Summary of Key Concepts

- People and environments can be described according to six categories of Realistic, Investigative, Artistic, Social, Enterprising, and Conventional. These are the RIASEC Codes.

- People and environments exhibit varying amounts of these interests, with some more dominant than others.

- When a person's interests are satisfied by the environment, there is congruence, and that congruence leads to job satisfaction and better job performance.

- It is important to understand how one's interests relate to occupations, education, training, hobbies, and leisure activities.

_____

Holland, J.L. (1997). *Making Vocational Choices – A Theory of Vocational Personalities and Work Environments. (3rd ed).* Odessa, FL. Psychological Assessment Resources.

Chapter 2:

Interest Activities and How to Use Them

This chapter includes more than 100 activities you can use to help students or clients identify and understand their interests and how those interests relate to their education, training, leisure activities, hobbies, jobs, and other life choices. The activities are grouped according to major theme or purpose including:

- **Measuring Interests**
- **School Subjects Activities**
- **Out of School Activities**
- **Education and Training Activities**
- **Occupations and Jobs Activities**
- **Career Planning**

Measuring Interests. This section includes some short interest checklists that you can use with your students giving them an indication of their major interest areas. Your students can use the results from these inventories for other activities within this book that suggest students use the checklist with family members, fellow students, and others. These checklists are quick and easy ways to determine interests. Informal data have been gathered that show good consistency between the results of these checklists and more sophisticated instruments, but they should not replace professionally developed and validated published inventories that are highlighted in Chapter 4. of this book.

In order to complete many of the activities in this section, students must be aware of their own interest areas, which can be determined through the completion of the inventories. They should also have a basic understanding of the general definitions or descriptions of these areas. At the end of this introductory section is a chart which provides a description of each of the interest areas. This chart can be reproduced and used by your students for reference as they proceed with the various activities.

School Subjects Activities. All activities have been designed to assist students in understanding how interests relate to school subjects, people in their school, technology, school clubs, and other school activities. For career guidance personnel who wish to integrate career development into other school subjects, a number of activities will help to do that. For example, activities in language arts, mathematics, fine arts, and social studies have been included with the suggestion that they be integrated into those classes. Teachers of various school subjects can use these activities to help integrate career concepts into their courses. Activities in this section should, therefore, help students understand how what they are doing in school is related to interests and occupations.

Out of School Activities. Activities relating to hobbies and leisure activities are part of this section. Exercises using TV programs, movies, birthday presents, hats worn by people in occupations, and other situations help to show students how interests permeate their social life and leisure activities. How hobbies can relate to jobs is included as a focus.

Education and Training Activities. This section includes activities that help students understand how school majors, training activities, and amount and level of education and training relate to occupations and their requirements. These activities can be used to help individuals understand that jobs and occupations are found in every interest area and every level of education. The activities can help students understand that, depending of their level of education and training, their options for working in various occupations and jobs differ greatly.

Occupations/Jobs Activities. Activities in this section emphasize how occupations in all interest areas are needed for the development of our economy. These activities also help students understand how some occupations have skill requirements that are similar, where occupational information can be found online, and how some jobs can be modified to accommodate flexible schedules, working at home, and persons with disabilities.

Career Planning. This section includes four generic career planning guides that can be used with elementary school, middle school, high school, and post-secondary school individuals. These career plans can help an individual organize and plan his or her goals, activities, and future plans. The forms should be modified to accommodate the needs of your target audience and your specific situation. Use what works for you, delete what doesn't, and add what seems relevant to the group you are working with.

Who Can Use These Activities?

These activities are designed for use primarily with middle school, secondary school, and post-secondary school students, but most can be used effectively at the elementary school level or with older adults. Some activities may require modification of vocabulary in order to be used at higher or lower levels. Elementary school students may require some additional explanation or monitoring to ensure they are completing the activity correctly. Regardless of the level, you should modify the exercise in any way that helps the students understand the task and gain useful information from it.

A few of the activities require Internet access so that certain web pages can be accessed. The web sites that are used belong to legitimate organizations such as the U.S. Department of Labor and are accurate as of this writing. You may wish to modify some of the exercises to place more focus on the resources in your own career center, library, or computerized career programs such as your state systems or commercial products that you may use in your career development program. The activities are very supportive and highly conducive to this type of modification.

Some activities have exercises that can be photocopied from the book and handed to students for completion.Other activities merely require a short verbal explanation to the students.

For clarity and ease of use, the word *students* has been used in the activities throughout the book, but many of the activities can also be used by career counselors who are working in private practice with clients as well as by other career development professionals.

How to Use These Activities

Clearly, you will not use all 101 activities with each of your students. You will need to select those that are most relevant to students based on their needs, level of career maturity, and the objectives of your career development program. The **Introduction** suggests several ways in which this book can support various objectives from selecting an interest inventory, to working with teachers in your school to show how interests relate to various school subjects, to individual career planning.

To manage time, you may wish to shorten selected exercises. This may be particularly important for younger students. Some of the exercises can be done in a career class and others during a school course. You may want to assign some exercises for students to do as projects and/or at home. How you use the activities is up to your good judgment based on your knowledge of the students with whom you work.

A few activities refer to **Appendix A**, a listing of occupation categories by RIASEC interest area. This listing was produced by the O*NET Occupational System created by the U.S. Department of Labor. You may wish to photocopy this appendix and make it available to students for those exercises. Instead of this appendix, you can elect to use other occupational listings found in your career resource center. If you choose to do that, be sure the activity is modified to accommodate that change.

Working with Your Students

All the activities are based on the assumption that you have spent some amount of time explaining interests to the students and how they relate to careers. A basic understanding of the **RIASEC** areas is critical. **Chapter 1** provides for you a basic overview of interests and why they are important in career development. The focus in that chapter is on the Holland Vocational Personality Theory, the most popular and researched interest structure for use in career development.

The exercises in this chapter are designed to supplement your explanation of interests, in order to specifically engage students in activities that can help them more fully understand those interest areas. The activities will help them see how those interests relate to school courses, majors, education and training, hobbies, occupations, leisure activities and life planning. The activities should be presented as interesting, helpful, and fun to use. They can be completed in school or as extracurricular activities.

It would be helpful to remind students that people have more than one interest area. Further, it is important to emphasize that people generally have some level of interest in all six **RIASEC** areas—some areas may just be stronger or more dominant in some people than in others. The same may be said for school subjects, hobbies, occupations, etc. For example, the same occupation may satisfy persons with differing interests. This condition, that people and occupations (or hobbies, courses, leisure activities, etc.) are not rigidly categorized, should serve as the basis for a healthy discussion among your students because reality does not often subject itself to "button holing" into neat and orderly categories. As a result, where an activity in this book asks for a classification of an occupation, a hobby, a training program, or school subjects to a single **RIASEC** category, there may be arguments for or against a classification. Good arguments could be provided for assigning more than one interest area to the occupation, hobby, training program, etc. Discuss with your students why they classified an occupation or hobby or activity into a particular interest category and be sure that they can provide good reasons for doing so.

Some of the activities can be used without students knowing their own interest areas, but they <u>must</u> have a basic understanding of the RIASEC interest areas to complete the activities. The chart describing the interest areas, found at the end of this introductory section, should be reproduced for the students so that they have a reference guide.

Several of the activities ask students to work with their own primary interest areas. These may be identified through the exercises located in the first section of this chapter, Measuring Interests. A more accurate assessment of interests can be obtained from using one of the methodically developed published inventories. Advice on how to select a good inventory is included in **Chapter 3**. Available inventories are described in **Chapter 4**.

To augment your discussions or to provide an avenue for obtaining further information related to the activities in this chapter, **Appendix B** can supplement the information you may have in your career center.

Summary of Interest Areas

Realistic people are often interested in mechanical activities. They frequently prefer activities that allow them to use their hands, let them see the results of their work, allow them to work alone rather than with others, and use machines, tools and equipment. Some examples of Realistic occupations include Aircraft Pilot, Automotive Mechanic, Broadcast Technician, Woodworker, Firefighter, and Radar Operator.

Investigative people are often interested in mathematical or scientific activities. They typically prefer activities that involve learning about new subjects or allow them to use their knowledge to solve problems or create new things and ideas. Some examples of Investigative occupations include Detective, Dietician, Nutritionist, Meteorologist, Physical Therapist, Psychologist, and Veterinarian.

Artistic people like activities that allow them to express themselves through some type of artistic medium. They typically like activities that allow them to be creative, to use their imagination to do something original, and to work according to their own rules. Some examples of Artistic occupations include Actor or Actress, Graphic Designer, Jeweler, Musician, Photographer, and Writer.

Conventional people often prefer activities that allow them to use organizational, clerical, and arithmetic skills. They often prefer activities that require attention to detail and accuracy. Some typical Conventional occupations include Accountant, Bank Teller, Budget Analyst, Computer Operator, Court Reporter, and Payroll Clerk.

Enterprising people tend to prefer activities that allow them to influence others. They frequently like activities that are fast-paced and require them to take on a lot of responsibility or leadership roles. Some typical Enterprising occupations include Executive, Judge, Real Estate Agent, Retail Buyer, Sales Representative, and Travel Agent.

Social people often prefer activities that allow them to interact with others. They frequently like activities that involve working with and helping others, and that involve teaching. Some examples of typical Social occupations include Counselor, Licensed Practical Nurse, Physical Therapy Assistant, Flight Attendant, Recreation Worker, and Teacher.

Source: U.S. Department of Defense, ASVAB Career Exploration Program.

Measuring Interests

This section contains the following reproducible student activities:

TITLE	DIRECTIONS
Activity #1 **What Is Your Primary Interest Area?**	Completing this instrument will give you and your students a good idea of their interest areas without the use of a lengthy or costly interest inventory. Make sufficient copies of this checklist for each of your students. Have them complete it. It should only take 10 minutes. Discuss their results and ask them if they learned anything new about themselves. This can be completed in class or as a homework assignment.
Activity #2 **Assessing What You Like**	Make sufficient copies of this checklist for your students. Ask them to complete the checklist and determine their primary interest area. Discuss how their results might explain their favorite school subjects, hobbies, or jobs they think they like.
Activity #3 **Your Family**	Make a copy of this checklist for each of your students. Ask them to pick a family member and guess his or her primary interest area. Then the student should ask that person to complete the checklist and score it. Have a discussion of the results with your students to include: Is the interest area of your family member the same or different from yours? If it is the same, what kinds of activities do you or would you like to do together? If it is different, what interest characteristics of the person stand out to you the most? How does the person use his or her interests – on the job, as a hobby? Did you guess the interest area correctly? This checklist can also be taken by your students to provide a quick overview of their own interest areas.

What Is Your Primary Interest Area?

Most people have more than one primary interest area. To learn what your strongest interest area is, pick the description that most closely resembles you. Place a #1 by the interest area that is most like you, a #2 by the interest area that is next most like you. Don't focus on what you do well, just think about what you like or prefer doing.

INTEREST AREAS

_____ **A.** I like to work with my hands using tools, machines, equipment, and materials. I prefer to work with animals or in the garden. I am best working with things, as opposed to ideas or people.

_____ **B.** I like to work on solving problems. My favorite subjects tend to be science and math related. I like to troubleshoot problems. I like to gather data about a problem and come up with a solution.

_____ **C.** I tend to be a creative person. Some of my very favorite activities would involve doing or performing dance, theater, writing, or the arts.

_____ **D.** I really like helping people. If people need help or advice, I am very happy to do what I can. I would like activities such as counseling people or tending to their needs.

_____ **E.** I really like to lead people to achieve a goal. Convincing people to do something I want them to do is fun for me. I like to sell ideas or things.

_____ **F.** I like working with details and numbers. For me, it is important that everything is in order and that certain standards are met and procedures are used.

If you picked A, your interest area is called **Realistic**
If you picked B, your interest area is called **Investigative**
If you picked C, your interest area is called **Artistic**
If you picked D, your interest area is called **Social**
If you picked E, your interest area is called **Enterprising**
If you picked F, your interest area is called **Conventional**

My #1 interest area is _____
This is called your primary interest area.

My #2 interest area is _____
This is called your secondary interest area.

Assessing What You Like

Most people have more than one primary interest area. To learn what your strongest interest area is, pick the description that most closely resembles you. Place a #1 by the interest area that is most like you, a #2 by the interest area that is next most like you. Don't focus on what you do well, just think about what you like or prefer doing.

A. _____ I like work activities that include practical, hands-on problems and solutions; I enjoy dealing with plants, animals, and real-world materials like wood, tools, and machinery; I enjoy outside work.

B. _____ I like activities that have to do with ideas and thinking more than with physical activity; I like to search for facts and figures; I like to figure out problems in my head rather than to persuade or lead people.

C. _____ I like to work with activities that deal with the artistic side of things, like forms, designs and patterns; I like self-expression in my activities; I prefer not to have too many rules.

D. _____ I like to help other people and promote learning and personal development; I like to communicate with others rather than work with things, machines, or data; I like to teach, advise people, help others and be of service.

E. _____ I like to persuade and lead people; I like to make decisions; I like to work on activities that deal with starting and carrying out project and business ventures; I like taking action and taking risks for profit.

F. _____ I like working with details and data rather than ideas; I like to follow and/or create set procedures and routines; I like to work with precise standards rather than judging things for myself.

If you picked A, your interest area is called **Realistic**
If you picked B, your interest area is called **Investigative**
If you picked C, your interest area is called **Artistic**
If you picked D, your interest area is called **Social**
If you picked E, your interest area is called **Enterprising**
If you picked F, your interest area is called **Conventional**

My #1 interest area is _____
This is called your primary interest area.

My #2 interest area is _____
This is called your secondary interest area.

Your Family

Based on what you know about interest areas, see if you can guess the interest area of ONE family member like your mother, father, sister, brother, aunt, uncle, foster parent, or cousin. Once you think you know, give him or her the checklist below and see if you are correct.

Place a check mark by the activities you like or think you might like to do.

A.
___ working in a carpenter shop
___ working with animals
___ repairing appliances
___ working with machines
___ painting houses
___ driving a taxi or truck
___ operating machinery in a factory
___ caring for lawns and landscape
___ fixing electronic equipment
___ putting products together in a factory

___ **Number of Checks**

B.
___ studying about stars and the moon
___ studying past civilizations
___ planning a research study
___ conducting experiments about animals
___ studying how the human body works
___ using a microscope to find viruses
___ collecting data and forming a conclusion
___ investigate the cause of a house fire
___ use instruments to predict the weather
___ work with equipment to identify diseases

___ **Number of Checks**

C.
___ write stories or songs
___ perform a song on stage
___ create a stage play
___ perform in a dance troupe
___ paint pictures
___ take photographs for a news magazine
___ write a book
___ play a musical instrument
___ conduct a band or orchestra
___ play in a band or orchestra

___ **Number of Checks**

D.
___ volunteer in a hospital
___ help people work their relationships
___ tutor children
___ teach someone to read
___ volunteer in a non-profit agency
___ help elderly people
___ give care to a disabled person
___ help people select a future career
___ teach in a school
___ help doctors take care of patients

___ **Number of Checks**

E.
___ sell new or used cars, trucks, or SUVs
___ manage a department store
___ market a new clothing line to stores
___ sell things like computer equipment or toys
___ be an officer in a club or organization
___ manage your own business
___ buy and sell stocks and bonds
___ show and sell houses
___ be an agent for an athlete or actor
___ give presentations about the product you are selling

___ **Number of Checks**

F.
___ file papers in an office
___ enter data into a computer program
___ schedule office meetings
___ operate a calculator
___ design an office filing system
___ take notes during a meeting
___ take inventories of items in a store
___ proofread forms
___ photocopy letters and reports
___ sort and distribute mail

___ **Number of Checks**

Your Family (continued)

Which area had the most checks? The one with the most checks is probably the main or primary interest area of the person completing the checklist. Which area had the second most number of checks? This is also an important interest area for that person.

If most check marks were in A, the interest area is **Realistic**
If most check marks were in B, the interest area is **Investigative**
If most check marks were in C, the interest area is **Artistic**
If most check marks were in D, the interest area is **Social**
If most check marks were in E, the interest area is **Enterprising**
If most check marks were in F, the interest area is **Conventional**

Remember that many people have more than one interest area and that is OK. No interest area is better than another.

Is the interest area of your family member the same or different from yours?

_____

If it is the same, what kinds of activities do you or would you like to do together?

_____

_____

_____

_____

If it is different, what interest characteristics of the person stand out to you the most?

_____

_____

_____

_____

How does the person use their interests – on the job, as a hobby?

_____

_____

_____

_____

Did you guess their interest area correctly?

_____

#4 Life Accelerator – An Online Interest Inventory

This site, http://www.navy.com/lifeaccelerator, sponsored by the U.S. Navy, offers a free online interest inventory that provides results useful for career exploration. There are items that ask about activities one likes to do, interests about areas one would like to learn, and occupations of interest.

Direct your students to the site and have them take the interest inventory and ask that it be scored. They will receive a profile of results similar to that below.

The results give students information about their relative strengths in the six RIASEC areas.

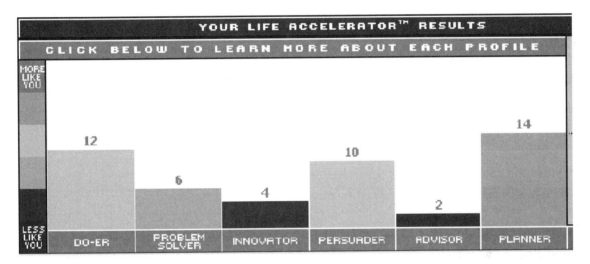

The labels are different, however. The translation between the Life Accelerator Results and the RIASEC Areas is listed below.

RIASEC Areas	Life Accelerator
Realistic	Do-Er
Investigative	Problem Solver
Artistic	Innovator
Social	Advisor
Enterprising	Persuader
Conventional	Planner

Discuss with your students how their results on the Life Accelerator are the same or different from those on other interest inventories.

#5 O*NET Interest Profiler

An instrument provided by the U.S. Department of Labor, the Interest Profiler, is available in print or computer version. Visit **http://www.onetcenter.org/IP.html** to download either or both versions.

If you download the paper version, you should make multiple copies and give the inventory to your students. The inventory is self-scored, so ask the students to complete the scoring and identify their top interest areas. The paper version is accompanied by a paper listing of occupations that match a person's interest profile while the automated version provides the information automatically. You can make multiple copies of the occupations listing and provide a copy to each student or just make a few for reference.

You or a student can download the automated version to a stand-alone computer. It can also be installed onto a network. Instructions for downloading are simple, but you may want to ask for assistance from a technology assistant or even one of your students.

The computer version automatically scores the interest inventory and provides a listing of matching occupations.

Discuss the results with your students. Did the results seem to describe them? Did the occupations seem reasonable?

Use your career center resources to help students find out more about occupations that look particularly intriguing.

School Subjects Activities

This section contains the following reproducible student activities:

TITLE	DIRECTIONS
Activity #6 **School Subjects**	Make copies of the activity for each student. Have them follow the directions to list favorite school subjects for each interest area. Students should have a basic understanding of the six interest areas before completing this exercise. Ask the students if their favorite school subjects seem to match their major interest areas. If they don't match, ask why they like that subject. Is it the teacher? Is it the teaching method? Were some interest areas more difficult to list school subjects? It may be difficult to find school subjects that relate to the interest area of Enterprising and maybe even Social. You should discuss this with your students. What implications might this have for students in these interest areas?
Activity #7 **Majors**	Make a copy of this activity for every student. Before the students complete the activity, discuss with the students each of the post-secondary majors and/or assign the students to do research on the majors. The goal here is to have the students develop a working knowledge of each major so that they understand how each relates to an interest area. After they complete the exercise, have them defend the reasons for matching the major with the interest area. Discuss how their interests will relate to decisions they make in the future.

Activity #8 **Want Ads**	Students can do this as a class activity or part of the activity can be assigned as homework. Have students create a graph showing the percent of their classmates in each of the six interest areas. This graph should be compared to the one that the class will create using their local newspaper job ads. If you use this as a "class" activity, be sure to have the students bring in the local newspaper. It is best that the newspaper really reflects your local area or neighborhood. If your local paper happens to be very substantial, you may wish to have the students use every other page or every third page in the want ads. You may wish to work with the mathematics teacher on this activity. Make a copy of the activity for each student. Have them create a graph of the results as per the directions. For help in creating a graph, go to the U.S. Department of Education's web site http://nces.ed.gov/nceskids/graphing/. This site will help students create various graphs including a bar graph, line graph, pie chart, and area graph. Discuss with students how the graph of their classmates compares to the graph of the want ads.
Activity #9 **Mathematics**	Distribute a copy of the activity to each student. After completing the activity, discuss with them the importance of math skills in occupations across all interest areas.
Activity #10 **What Does It Take?**	Distribute a copy of the activity to each student. After they complete the exercise, help them understand the relationship between high school and post-secondary school courses and the occupations. Ask them to determine what special training might be required and which occupations may require special licensing or certification.
Activity #11 **Be A Career Counselor**	Distribute a copy of the activity to each student. Have students pair up to complete the activity. You may need to give the students a copy of one of the checklists provided in the first section of this chapter, Measuring Interests. Through discussion of the results, help students understand the importance of occupational information and the match between the requirements of an occupation and the skills of a person.

Activity #12 **What Do You Do With Data**	Distribute a copy of the activity to each student. After they complete the exercise, discuss with them how data play a role in many occupations in all six interest areas.
Activity #13 **The Employees You Know**	Distribute a copy of the activity to each student. Work with students to identify the occupations of the employees in your school. After identifying the interest areas for each of these occupations, have them graph the results. A graphing program can be found at the U.S. Department of Education's web site http://nces.ed.gov/nceskids/graphing/. This site will help students create various graphs including a bar graph, line graph, pie chart, and area graph. Working with the math teacher, discuss what type of graph best represents the information.
Activity #14 **Word Play Nouns**	Distribute a copy of the activity to each student. After completion of the activity, ask the students to defend why they labeled the groups of words the way they did. Do any of the words fit in other interest categories?
Activity #15 **Word Play Verbs**	Distribute a copy of the activity to each student. After completion of the exercise, ask the students to defend why they labeled the groups of words the way they did. Do any of the words fit in other interest categories?

School Subjects

List as many school subjects as you can that a person in each of the following interest areas is likely to enjoy.

Realistic   Likes to work with objects, tools, machines, and animals and tends to dislike educational or therapeutic activities. Use of hands and equipment is typical.

_____

_____

Investigative   Includes activities that use creative investigation of physical, biological, and cultural situations in order to understand them. Problem solving is typical.

_____

_____

Artistic   Likes to work in creative activities using physical, verbal, or human materials to create art forms or products. The production of beautiful, creative, and/or unique outcomes is typical.

_____

_____

Social   Prefers to interact with people to inform, train, develop, cure, serve, or help.

_____

_____

Enterprising   Likes activities involving persuading or leading others toward achieving a goal. Selling things or ideas are preferred activities.

_____

_____

Conventional   Prefers activities involving detail work on tasks such as keeping records, filing materials, reproducing materials, organizing written and numerical data according to a particular plan. Operating business machines and data processing machines are preferred activities.

_____

_____

What are your favorite school subjects?_____

How do you think your favorite school subjects will relate to the career that you choose?

_____

_____

Were some interest areas more difficult to associate with school subjects? _____

Why do you think this is? _____

_____

Majors

Match post-secondary majors with the interest area by drawing a line from the major to the primary interest area.

Interest Areas	Post-secondary Majors
	Elementary Education
Realistic	Astronomy
	English
Investigative	Accounting
	Automotive Sciences
Artistic	Veterinary Medicine
	Marketing
Social	Public Relations
	Physics
Enterprising	Library Science
	Nursing
Conventional	Performing Arts

Did some majors seem to fit in more than one category? If so, which ones?

_____

_____

_____

_____

Want Ads

Look at your local newspaper. Read the want ads and classify each job by primary RIASEC area. Calculate the percentage of jobs in each interest area and then create a graph showing the percentage of occupations in each of the 6 areas. Compare this graph with the graph showing the percentage of your classmates in each interest area.

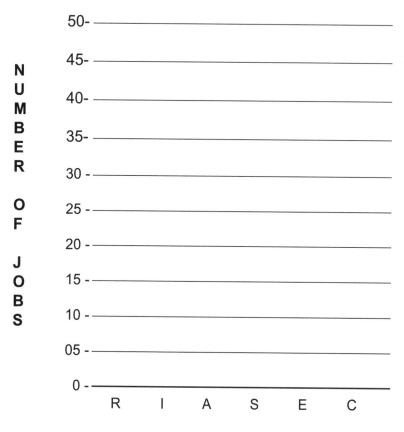

How do the graphs of the want ads and the graph of your classmates compare?

_____

_____

In what interest areas are the percentages most different?

_____

_____

What does this mean with respect to people being able to work in the jobs that match their interests in your local area?

_____

_____

Do you think it will be difficult or easy to find work in a job that matches your interest?

_____

Mathematics

Look at the following occupations. Identify the primary interest area of the occupation and list it in the box provided. Use R for Realistic, I for Investigative, A for Artistic, S for Social, E for Enterprising, and C for Conventional. Then, using your career center resources or www.online.onetcenter.org, identify how mathematics is used in each occupation.

Interest	Occupation	How Mathematics Is Used
	Medical and Clinical Laboratory Technicians	
	Electrical Engineers	
	Computer Systems Analyst	
	Forensic Science Technicians	
	Fashion Designers	
	Landscape Architects	
	Home Health Aids	
	Park Naturalists	
	Credit Authorizers	
	Management Analysts	
	Bill and Account Collectors	
	Economists	

Pick an occupation you are thinking about for a career and describe how mathematics is used by a person in that occupation.

_____

_____

_____

_____

What Does It Take?

Below is a list of occupations. Circle your top two interest areas and then, using your career center resources or www.online.onetcenter.org for research and reference, answer the following questions for the occupations you circled. In other words, if your top two interest areas are Conventional -C and Realistic- R, only pick the occupations listed in those two groups.

Realistic	**Carpenters** **Barbers** **Electrical Engineers**
Investigative	**Chemical Technicians** **Respiratory Therapists** **Surveyors**
Artistic	**Make Up Artists** **Talent Directors** **Composers**
Social	**Flight Attendants** **Dental Hygienists** **Physical Therapists**
Enterprising	**Telemarketers** **Travel Agents** **Ship Pilots**
Conventional	**Credit Checkers** **Tax Preparers** **Economists**

What high school classes would be most helpful for qualifying you for these occupations? _____

_____

What post-secondary classes would be most helpful for qualifying you for these occupations? _____

_____

What specific training programs are necessary to enter the occupations?

_____

Which occupations require a license before you can work in the occupation?

_____

Be a Career Counselor

With your partner, share what your primary interest areas are. Be sure to discuss any experience, education, skills, and training you might have that relates to your interest area. Then on the list below, circle your partner's interest area. Based on what your partner has just shared, choose one of the occupations in that interest area on which to counsel your partner. For example, if your partner is an S – Social, then counsel him or her on what skills and education would be needed to qualify for either Personnel Recruiter or Registered Nurse. Before role-playing the counseling session, learn about the occupations from your career center or www.online.onetcenter.org.

Interest Area	Occupations
Realistic	Dental Laboratory Technician Radiologic Technician
Investigative	Fish and Game Warden Geologist
Artistic	Actor Poet
Social	Personnel Recruiter Registered Nurse
Enterprising	Bailiff Athletic Coaches and Scout
Conventional	Fire Inspector Insurance Underwriter

As you research the occupation on which you will counsel your partner, write any notes here that will help you remember what to say.

What Do You Do with Data?

Look up information about the following occupations in your career center or on the Internet. What is the primary interest area of these occupations? List the interest areas Realistic, Investigative, Artistic, Social, Enterprising, or Conventional in the space provided. Next, determine how each of these occupations uses data or facts. List that information in the space provided on the right.

Interest Area	Occupation	How Data Are Used
	General Farm Workers	
	Pest Control Workers	
	Surveyors	
	Archivists	
	Stone Cutters and Carvers	
	Technical Writers	
	Animal Control Workers	
	Athletic Trainers	
	Bill and Account Collectors	
	Sales Managers	
	File Clerks	
	Astronomers	

How important are data to these occupations? _____

_____

What kinds of data are used by persons in each occupation? _____

_____

The Employees You Know

On a separate piece of paper, list the occupations of the people working in your school. Consider everyone that keeps your school going on a daily basis including the principal, school board members, teachers, food service persons, counselors, cleaning crew, etc. These are people that enable you to concentrate on your job—learning. Identify the primary interest areas of those occupations. Create a graph that shows the number of occupations in each of the six interest areas. Are there significant differences in the numbers for each interest area? For example are their more R (Realistic) occupations? More I (Investigative) occupations? What conclusions can you draw from this information?

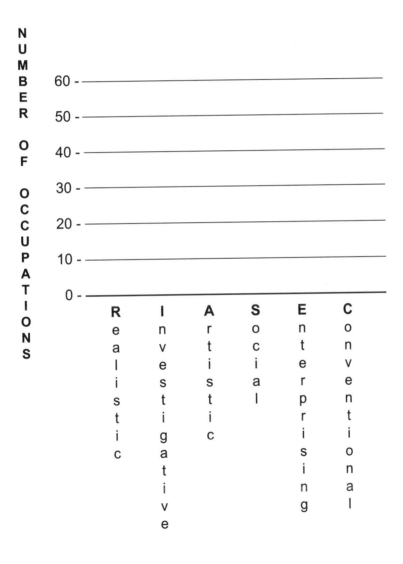

Word Play – Nouns

Below are groups of nouns describing data, people, things, and ideas. For each group, identify the primary interest area most typically associated with the word groups. Place your choice in the space above the group of words. The interest areas are Realistic, Investigative, Artistic, Social, Enterprising, and Conventional.

_____

words
symbols
knowledge
facts
numbers
experiments

_____

young adults
older people
ill individuals
handicapped people
teachers
counselors

_____

electric sockets
machines
forklift trucks
chain saws
electric motors
gas turbines

_____

word processors
regulations
reports
calculators
procedures
photocopy machines

_____

stock figures
policies
leaders
vision
extroverts
risk takers

_____

free spirits
dancers
fantasies
paint brush and pallet
stage
composition

Circle the group of words that appeals to you most.

Think of a good friend of yours. Which group of words do you think apply most to him or her? _____

_____

Think of a family member. Which group of words do you think apply most to him or her?

_____

_____

Word Play – Verbs

Below are groups of verbs describing data, people, things, and ideas. For each group, identify the primary interest area most typically associated with the word groups. Place your choice in the space above the group of words. The interest areas are Realistic, Investigative, Artistic, Social, Enterprising, and Conventional.

_____	_____	_____
fix	design	manage
assemble	paint	persuade
operate	write	supervise
load	sing	negotiate
carry	whirl	lead

_____	_____	_____
examine	serve	count
theorize	help	add
synthesize	treat	budget
experiment	teach	instruct
problem-solve	coach	file

Circle the group of words that appeals to you most.

Think of a good friend of yours. Which group of words do you think apply most to him or her? _____

_____

Think of a family member. Which group of words do you think apply most to him or her?

_____

_____

#16 Technology

Have students speculate and discuss with classmates how technology is or can be used in each of the six RIASEC areas. For example, ask students to discuss how a computer, word processing program, graphics program, Internet connection, spreadsheet, etc. can be used in occupations that span the six interest areas. Would a person in an Investigative occupation use a computer differently than a person in an Artistic occupation? How are the uses different? Would some aspects of technology be more frequent in occupations of one interest area than another? Which ones?

#17 School Clubs

Prepare a comprehensive list of school clubs and extracurricular activities in your school. Give the list of clubs and activities to the students and ask them to classify each club and activity according to the primary interest area.

As a project, have students administer one of the interest inventories in the first section of this chapter to students in several of the clubs.

Determine whether or not most of the members have the same primary interest area as the club. For example, do most members of the Future Teachers organization indicate that they have "Social" as their primary interest area?

#18 Current Events

Have students select a major article in a current issue of a local or national newspaper. Have them determine what people are mentioned in the article. Have students identify their job titles and occupations. Identify the primary interest areas of the occupations. Have a discussion with students to determine if there is a difference between a job title and an occupation.

#19 Create a Person with Creative Writing

You can involve the English or creative writing teacher with this activity.

Part 1: Have students pick one of the six interest areas and create a story about a fictitious individual who has that interest. Have students give the person a name and some descriptive characteristics. Suggest that students think about: What are his or her hobbies? What kinds of activities does person like? What are the favorite classes? What kinds of future jobs would he or she be most interested in preparing for? What might the person do on weekends that fit into that interest area? What kind of clubs would the person belong to? What might the person avoid doing?

Part 2: Once students have completed this exercise, have them exchange stories with a partner. Ask the partner to see if they can identify the interest area of the person in the story.

#20 A History Major

You may want to work with the school's social studies teacher on this activity.

Have the students think about what jobs or careers are available to history majors. Some possibilities include foreign service officer, lawyer, research assistant, teacher, and writer.

Have students identify the primary interest area for each of these occupations. Even though they all have history as a common thread, are the primary interest areas the same or different?

Have the students think about other occupations where having a history major is helpful.

#21 Talent Show

Working with the students' drama teacher, have the students perform the following activity. Tell them that they have been appointed to be the talent director for the school's talent show. The major responsibility is to include talents from each of the primary interest areas – Realistic, Investigative, Artistic, Social, Enterprising, and Conventional. Select the performers and describe what they would do and how they would entertain the audience.

#22 Creating a Job Ad

You may wish to work with the school newspaper's faculty advisor on this activity.

Divide the class into six teams. Assign one of the occupations listed below to each team. Have the students use your career center resources or information from the Internet to create a newspaper classified ad for the occupation assigned to their group. When the exercise is complete, have each of the teams present their classified ad to the other students and have those students guess the interest area the job in the ad represents.

Electricians
Dentists
Drama Teacher
History Teacher
Mediator
Controller

#23 Inspirations

Keep pace with the drummer you hear, however measured or far away.
—Henry David Thoreau

There is only one success—to be able to spend your life in your own way.
—Christopher Morely

Choose a job you love, and you will never have to work a day in your life.
—Confucius

Write these inspirations on the blackboard. Have students read the inspirations and write a paragraph about what they mean, how they apply to them, and how they involve their primary interest area.

Ask the students which of the sayings is most meaningful to them. Discuss why it is important to choose an occupation or activity that is important and meaningful. Ask students if they think it is important to have a job that they would love, or a job that someone else may want them to have.

You may wish to select other inspirations as substitutes for the ones provided.

#24 Biographies and Autobiographies

You may wish to work with the English teacher on this activity. He or she may have suggestions for using books other than those listed, or you may want to select different books from the list below that might be more appropriate for your students. For students at the elementary and middle school levels, work with a teacher to identify books that are grade appropriate.

Below is a list of books that you can use; they have been popular books in the past. Have the students read one of the biographies and identify the probable interest areas of the person.

The Price of Loyalty: George W. Bush, the White House, and the Education of Paul O'Neill by Paul O'Neill.

Going for the Gold: Sarah Hughes: America's Sweetheart by R. S. Ashby

The Tree of Life: Charles Darwin by Peter Sis

Buffett: The Making of an American Capitalist by Roger Lowenstein

Living History by Hillary Rodham Clinton

Benjamin Franklin: An American Life by Walter Isaacson

Leonardo: The Artist and the Man by Sergey Bramley

My Life by William J. Clinton

Discuss the following questions with students: What information from the book led you to believe that the key person could be categorized by the interest areas you identified? List some words used in the book to describe the main character that helped you determine his or her interest area.

#25 National Issues

You may wish to work with the social studies teacher on this activity.

The following issues are situations that worry our government and our citizenry – childhood obesity, global warming, depletion of our natural resources, and environmental pollution. Have students research one of these problems and identify 10 occupations that are needed to help solve the problem. Ask students to classify those occupations by primary interest area. Discuss with them any trends that they see and ask them to determine the training and education requirements of those occupations.

#26 Collage

You may wish to work with the art teacher on this activity.

Using magazines, have students cut out pictures of people working in occupations in each of the six primary interest areas and create a collage. Discuss with the students what aspect of the picture gave them an indication of the person's occupation. Have the students exchange their collage with a partner and ask the partner if they can identify the occupations and the associated interest areas.

#27 Poetic Verse

You may wish to work with the English teacher on this activity.

Ask each student to select an occupation in his or her interest area and write a poem about it. Use any poetic form. Have the students read their poems and see if the class can identify the occupation and the interest area the poems represent.

#28 Autobiography

You may wish to work with the English teacher on this activity.

Using autobiography as the narrative form, have students write a passage about themselves as they work in the occupation of their dreams. They should describe themselves as they first enter the occupation, as they progress up the ladder with promotions, and what they would be doing as they approach retirement age. Ask them to contrast their lives when they first entered this occupation versus what their lives were like at the time of retirement. Ask them to also describe how their career journeys related to their primary interest area.

Allow time for the students to share their autobiography with the rest of the class. Conclude by discussing how they see how their lives changed throughout their career journeys. Ask the students how their primary interest areas related to their dream jobs and how it would influence what they do on their jobs and in their lives.

#29 Cinematic Expression

This activity can be performed by individual students or in teams. If the students are in teams, they should be grouped by similar interest areas.

Using a camcorder, have students create a 10-minute movie about a day-in-the-life of a person in an occupation involving their primary interest area. Have the students show the film to their classmates and ask the viewers to determine the primary interest area that was intended. Have the students speculate about the amount of education and training that each job requires.

#30 What's My Line?

Divide your group into teams of three. Assign an occupation to each team and have them research what a person in the occupation does, what kind of training is needed, what kind of tools are used, etc. Have each team sit at the front of the class and let the remainder of the class ask questions about the occupation until the occupation is guessed. The questions should be yes or no questions and should involve factors such as primary interest area, amount of education required, major tasks, work values, typical tools used, etc. For example, some possible questions could be "Does your occupation require a bachelor's degree?" or "Is the occupation generally performed outside?"

#31 Why This Major?

For students who have selected a post-secondary major, have them make an oral presentation or write a paper about why they selected this major and how it satisfies their primary interest area. If it does not match their primary interest area, have them describe what other factors influenced their decision. Ask them if they expect to encounter any issues or problems if they select an occupation outside their primary interest area.

#32 Sing a Song

Have students compose a song that describes their ideal occupation and why it satisfies their primary interest area. Have them perform the song in front of the class and ask the class members to identify the interest area of that occupation. The composer should be asked what characteristics of the occupation make it seem ideal to him or her.

#33 Cartooning

Have students create a cartoon or caricature about a person working in an occupation in his or her primary interest area. As a class project, have the students create a printed or virtual publication. Through a discussion with the students determine what aspects of the person working in the occupation were exaggerated in the cartoon. Ask why this characteristic was chosen.

#34 Charting a Company

You may wish to work with the math teacher and/or the business teacher on this activity.

Have students select a small company in your local area. Have them list the occupations of people working in that company. Using that list, have them identify the primary interest areas of each of those occupations.

Have students create a graph that shows the distribution of occupations across the six interest areas. Discuss the distribution of occupations. Are the occupations found predominantly in a few interest categories or are they spread across all six?

Have students complete the activity titled *The Employees You Know* found earlier in this book. How do the results of the company graph compare to one that describes your school? What are the similarities? The differences?

#35 Poster People

Have students work in teams organized according to their primary interest area. Ask the students to create a poster advertising the characteristics of people and jobs in that primary interest area. For example, Investigative might have pictures of scientists, laboratories, space ships, etc. Using the poster, have the students briefly present why individuals should go into occupations in the selected interest area. Ask them to explain what it is about the interest area that is engaging, fun, rewarding, etc.

#36 Comparing and Contrasting

Ask students to interview two people who are working in occupations that are in different interest areas. Have the students write an essay or create a chart showing the differences and similarities of how each person feels about his or her job. Have students look for such things as what people do on the job, how much they are paid, why they picked that occupation, how they prepared for it, how their life styles are the same or different, their work schedules, what equipment they use, etc.

Ask the students if there are similarities of the people and/or the occupations even if they are in different interest areas. Discuss with the students the major differences between the two people and their occupations. Ask the students what was most surprising to them as they learned about the people they were interviewing.

#37 Marketing Yourself

The Pepsi Generation; You're in Good Hands with Allstate; Be All that You Can Be

These are a few marketing slogans that you hear on television and see in the newspapers. Ask students to create a marketing slogan for themselves that incorporates some aspect of their primary interest area.

Have the students read the slogans to the entire class and have the class try to guess the primary interest area represented by the slogan. Ask the presenters to explain how the slogan represents their primary interest areas.

Out of School Activities

This section contains the following reproducible student activities:

TITLE	DIRECTIONS
Activity #38 **Matching Interests with Activities**	Distribute a copy of the activity to each student. After they complete the activity, ask them to defend their answers. Note how some activities can be properly categorized into more than one area.
Activity #39 **Hobbies as Careers**	Distribute a copy of the activity to each student. Where appropriate have them read the article in the Occupational Outlook Quarterly on hobbies to careers. It can be found at http://www.bls.gov/opub/ooq/2001/Fall/art01.pdf. You may want to have students research the characteristics of their hobby before completing this activity. Discuss with students the reasoning behind their answers.
Activity #40 **Birthday Presents**	Distribute a copy of the activity to each student. Indicate that the sheet provides a list of possible birthday presents that someone could give and receive. They need to think about the present and make a determination as to the interest area of the person who may like to receive that gift. Make it a point to discuss how persons in more than one interest area could appreciate the presents. Have the students defend their decisions.
Activity #41 **Hobbies**	Distribute a copy of the activity to each student. Have them think about the various tasks or actions that a person having that hobby would perform. Then they should identify the related interest area of that hobby. Ask the students to share their thinking about the tasks involved with each hobby and why they chose the interest areas they did. Discuss how various hobbies can reflect several different interest areas.

Activity #42 **Hats**	Distribute a copy of the activity to each student. Start a discussion on how various hats are worn by people in certain occupations. Students may need to look up information on some of the hats. Searching for "hats" on the Internet is a good starting point.
Activity #43 **Word Search**	Make a copy of this page for each student. They need to find the words Realistic, Investigative, Artistic, Social, Enterprising, and Conventional within this anagram. The words can be horizontal, vertical, diagonal, and backwards. The answers to this exercise are provided for you so that you can help students that can't quite complete the exercise.

Matching Interests with Activities

Match the Interest Area with the activity. Are the activities Realistic, Investigative, Artistic, Social, Enterprising, or Conventional? List the interest area in the space provided next to each activity.

_____ **Build shelves or cabinets**

_____ **Plan an experiment**

_____ **Market cell phone service over the telephone**

_____ **Paint a picture**

_____ **Volunteer at a hospital**

_____ **Keep a ledger of expenses**

_____ **Fix a broken piece of equipment**

_____ **Run a newspaper stand**

_____ **Be an officer in a school club**

_____ **Teach children how to read**

_____ **Proofread magazine articles**

_____ **Manage a store**

_____ **Operate a business**

_____ **Study astronomy**

_____ **Repair appliances**

_____ **Direct a play**

_____ **Write a novel or a poem**

_____ **Help people with disabilities**

_____ **Study rocks from the moon**

_____ **Program a computer**

Hobbies as Careers

Can you be paid for having fun? Sure! Your jobs should be fun for you. If you want to have a job that matches your interests, think about the hobbies you have. Do your hobbies seem to translate to jobs? Do you think people will pay you to work on your hobbies?   In the chart below, list your hobbies and then list the possible careers that you might pursue. You may need to do some research about your hobby to see what aspects of it might be useful on the job. If you don't have any hobbies, list some areas of interest that you might have, like reading, listening to music, dancing, sports, etc.

Hobby	Career Possibilities
1.	1. 2. 3.
2.	1. 2. 3.
3.	1. 2. 3.

Birthday Presents

Using six different colored pencils or crayons, one color for each interest area, draw a line between the interest area and various birthday presents that a person with that primary interest area might like to receive. Some birthday presents would be appreciated by people in more than one interest area. Can you identify these?

Realistic

Investigative

Artistic

Social

Enterprising

Conventional

tennis racket

tickets to a play

telescope

dark suit and tie

nursing uniform

word processing program

toolbox

motivational tape

music CD

cookbook

computer graphics program

karaoke machine

paint kit with brushes and watercolors

programmable calculator

microscope

book of poetry

brief case and cell phone

Hobbies

Look at the list of hobbies or extracurricular activities listed below. Think about the different tasks or actions that a person having each hobby would engage in and list those actions to the right of each hobby. Next, match the hobby or extracurricular activity to the primary interest area by placing an R for Realistic, I for Investigative, A for Artistic, S for Social, E for Enterprising, or C for Conventional to the left of each hobby.

Interest Area	Hobby or Activity	Tasks or Actions
	photography	
	bowling	
	ice hockey	
	selling Girl Scout cookies	
	building a birdhouse	
	rock collecting	
	dancing	
	constructing model cars	
	pottery	
	stamp collecting	
	gardening	
	genealogy	
	candle making	
	puppetry	
	birding	
	magic	
	ham radio	
	computer games	

What's your hobby? _____

How would you label it by its primary interest area? _____

Hats

Below is a list of hats that might be used by people in various jobs. On the line to the right, list an occupation in which a person might wear the hat. Then match each hat with the major Interest area. List the interest area on the space provided on the left— Realistic, Investigative, Artistic, Social, Enterprising, and Conventional.

_____ **hard hat** _____

_____ **astronaut helmet** _____

_____ **beret** _____

_____ **eye shade/visor** _____

_____ **top hat** _____

_____ **miner's light** _____

_____ **nurse's cap** _____

_____ **football helmet** _____

_____ **skull cap/zucchetto/turban** _____

_____ **cowboy hat** _____

_____ **baseball cap** _____

_____ **police hat** _____

_____ **chef's hat** _____

_____ **earmuffs** _____

_____ **firefighter's hat** _____

_____ **clown hat** _____

_____ **straw hat** _____

Think about a job in your primary interest area that you might like to have some day. What kind of hat would you be wearing? _____

Describe your job. _____

_____

_____

Word Search

Find and circle the word representing the six basic interest areas of Realistic, Investigative, Artistic, Social, Enterprising, and Conventional. The words can be horizontal, vertical or diagonal.

```
G O R T I M V T R Q L C M S H G K E O T H F K S L A I C O S O L L H K D H H A N T K Z
I K W O T H D L W L G L D J S K D L W I G I W P A M D Q P F I E N C X K R L S K E F K
Q N E R N C B S M E O F H V L W J C I E O G F L D L C M S N Z V X D S R Q U R O T U I
D K V H W L L F J H L W R J G O S M N F L S P L F J T O W R P S L F J G H E Y T W E S
F J S E C B N V B D G R T T I Y M W H D T W L H O E J C N X M F R W T W B F J T I D N
N F J D S W O S K F H T I O Q H D J S L E H T G N I S I R P R E T N E J W I Q P J G L
J J D K A T E U D K G H E I P D J G O E P Q F L S K S N C N D A H E Y W I S J F H W O
K R E I W Y I H Q K W P F L O G K J E M W J D K G L H O T L U Q H D K G L Y P R K S J
D K I M R E A G I S T I C V M R E A L I S T I C L M N B C V X Z I O W E W T R Y G I P
P O I U H K F J A R T I S T I C C N V H F Y R E T E E S W S K L L M C J D U K E H F H
P M I L P D K S J T M C N D J E U Y Y S J N F B F H E T T G W V D B F N D M W N F B D
I M D F N G H E J E I U D H S K S E K F J C O N V E N T I O N A L M M C B K G L C B N
M S E I J W G I E U V V U D H W S U W U I R H D C G S J D K G K G K G K D S J S H S H
F J D K L S J F K D L E E I E P S K F J G H E J W L K W L F K F J D S J S H F J F K D
```

Word Search Answers

```
G O R T I M V T R Q L C M S H G K E O T H F K S L A I C O S O L L H K D H H A N T K Z
I K W O T H D L W L G L D J S K D L W I G I W P A M D Q P F I E N C X K R L S K E F K
Q N E R N C B S M E O F H V L W J C I E O G F L D L C M S N Z V X D S R Q U R O T U I
D K V H W L L F J H L W R J G O S M N F L S P L F J T O W R P S L F J G H E Y T W E S
F J S E C B N V B D G R T T I Y M W H D T W L H O E J C N X M F R W T W B F J T I D N
N F J D S W O S K F H T I O Q H D J S L E H T G N I S I R P R E T N E J W I Q P J G L
J J D K A T E U D K G H E I P D J G O E P Q F L S K S N C N D A H E Y W I S J F H W O
K R E I W Y I H Q K W P F L O G K J E M W J D K G L H O T L U Q H D K G L Y P R K S J
D K I M R E A G I S T I C V M R E A L I S T I C L M N B C V X Z I O W E W T R Y G I P
P O I U H K F J A R T I S T I C C N V H F Y R E T E E S W S K L L M C J D U K E H F H
P M I L P D K S J T M C N D J E U Y Y S J N F B F H E T T G W V D B F N D M W N F B D
I M D F N G H E J E I U D H S K S E K F J C O N V E N T I O N A L M M C B K G L C B N
M S E I J W G I E U V V U D H W S U W U I R H D C G S J D K G K G K G K D S J S H S H
F J D K L S J F K D L E E I E P S K F J G H E J W L K W L F K F J D S J S H F J F K D
```

#44 Picture This

You might want to work with the art teacher on this activity.

Identify some pieces of artwork in each of the six interest areas of Realistic (R), Investigative (I), Artistic (A), Social (S), Enterprising (E), and Conventional (C). Show the pieces of art and ask the students to determine the interest area that each piece of art represents.

Possible pieces of artwork include:

Dance Class at the Opera by Degas; Musee d'Orsay, Paris (found at http://www.musee- orsay.fr)

Liberty Leading People by Delecroix; Louvre Museum, Paris (found at http://www.louvre.fr/louvrea.htm)

Space Phenomenon Imitates Art in Universe Version of Van Gogh Painting, retrieved from HubbleSite.org

St. John the Baptist, by Girardon; Louvre Museum, Paris (found at http://www.louvre.fr/louvrea.htm)

The Harvesters by Bruegel the Elder; Louvre Museum, Paris (found at http://www.louvre.fr/louvrea.htm)

The Lace Maker by Vermeer; Louvre Museum, Paris (found at http://www.louvre.fr/louvrea.htm)

The Banker and His Wife by Metsys; Louvre Museum, Paris (found at http://www.louvre.fr/louvrea.htm)

Little Dancer Aged Fourteen by Degas; Clark Art Institute; Williamstown MA (found at clarkart.edu)

As an alternative activity, ask the students to locate a piece of art that represents their primary interest areas. Their selections can come from art books or web sites, or this activity can be conducted during a visit to a local art museum. Have them present their selections to the class and ask the class to identify the interest area the piece of art represents. Have the students explain how they see their interest areas represented by the piece of artwork they have chosen.

#45 When Retirement Comes

Have students interview three retired people to determine how they are using their time. They should determine whether or not each person is working for pay, volunteering, pursuing hobbies, spending time on leisure activities, or pursuing other interests. The students should determine how the retired person's activities relate to his or her primary interest area by having the person complete one of the checklists of inventories in the Measuring Interests Section of this chapter.

After reporting on their interview findings to the class, have the students project what they might do at the time they elect to retire. What hobbies will they pursue? Will they have a part-time job? If so, what? How will what the student thinks they will do relate to their primary interest area? You can elicit this information in a discussion or have them write an essay on the subject.

#46 Cinema Winners

List the films that have received Oscar nominations for "Best Picture" this past year. Have students identify the occupations portrayed in each film. List the occupations and match the occupation to the primary interest area.

Engage the students in a discussion about what characteristics of the persons in the film led them to believe that the occupation was in a particular interest area. Were some occupations difficult to identify? Were some occupations unusual for this day and age?

#47 TV Programs

Have the students agree on their favorite three television programs. This can be done through a brief discussion and compiling a class list of favorites and then a class vote for the top three. Ask the students to identify the occupations of the major characters in each show and match the occupation according to its primary interest area. Ask the following if they apply: On television are there particular occupations that seem to be represented more than others? Are there particular interest areas that seem to be more prevalent than others? Do the occupations represented on television seem to be similar or different from what is typical in our society; in your family?

#48 Tradeoffs

For a variety of reasons, it is not unusual for a person who has a strong interest in one interest area to have to work in another interest area. Have students indicate how they might satisfy their interests outside the job in the following situations:

Your interest area is Social and you have to work in a Realistic job.

Your interest area is Artistic and you are working in a Conventional job.

Your interest area is Investigative and you are working in an Enterprising job.

Your interest area is Realistic and you have to work in an Artistic job.

Your interest area is Conventional and you have to work in an Artistic job.

Your interest area is Enterprising and you have to work in an Investigative job.

Are there ways that you might be able to modify the job to incorporate your primary interest area?

Have the students indicate their answers in a class discussion so that all students can benefit from the thinking of the other students.

#49 Identifying the Interests of Other People

Have students interview three friends in order to identify their major interest area.

Some question they can ask:

What are your favorite hobbies?
What are your favorite school classes?
What activities do you like to do in your spare time?
What kind of jobs are you interested in?

After the students have conducted the interviews and made a determination of what the interest area is for each person, have the students administer one of the checklists in the first section of this chapter, such as "What is Your Primary Interest Area?" or "Assessing What You Like" to each of their three friends. Have the students report back to class by comparing their initial belief with the results of the checklist. Discuss any surprises and/or consistencies.

Education and Training Activities

This section contains the following reproducible student activities:

TITLE	DIRECTIONS
Activity #50 **College Majors**	Distribute a copy of this page to each student. Suggest that the selection of a college major often depends on one's interests. Discuss with the students how their interests will direct them to certain college majors.
Activity #51 **How Much Education**	Distribute a copy of the activity to each student. Ask them to discuss how education relates to career choice. Ask them if there seems to be a relationship between education and interest area.
Activity #52 **Online Degrees**	Distribute a copy of the activity to each student. When talking about how further education might be obtained through online programs, see if the students can classify the programs by RIASEC area. Discuss with the students their reasoning behind choosing one interest area over another.
Activity #53 **Jobs Requiring Less Than a Bachelor's Degree**	Distribute a copy of the activity to each student. After completing the exercise, see if students can identify any interest area trends. Is one interest area represented more than others in the list?

Activity #54 **High Growth Jobs Requiring an Associate Degree or Post-secondary Vocational Degree**	Distribute a copy of the activity to each student. Discuss with students what they conclude with respect to the interest areas in this category. Which interest areas are represented most on the list? Which ones are missing?
Activity 55 **High Growth Jobs Requiring a Bachelor's Degree**	Distribute a copy of the activity to each student. Discuss with students what they conclude with respect to the interest areas in this category. Which interest areas are represented most on the list? Which ones are missing?
Activity #56 **High Growth Jobs Requiring a Graduate Degree**	Distribute a copy of the activity to each student. Discuss with students what they conclude with respect to the interest areas in this category. Which interest areas are represented most on the list? Which ones are missing?

College Majors

The following is a list of college majors. Match each college major with the primary interest area. Draw a line between the interest area and the college major that a person with that interest area would likely pursue. There will be more than one college major for each interest area.

Interest Area	Major
	Mathematics
REALISTIC	Elementary Education
	Economics
	Public Relations
INVESTIGATIVE	Marketing
	Civil Engineering
	Biology
ARTISTIC	Environmental Science
	Genetics
	Philosophy
SOCIAL	English
	Psychology
	Material Sciences
ENTERPRISING	Drama
	Performing Arts
	Geology
CONVENTIONAL	Art Education
	Medical Science
	Political Science

If the college major you are considering is in this list, draw a circle around it. If it is not

in this list, write it here: _____. In what interest area is your college

major? _____. What is your primary interest area? _____.

Are they the same? _____.

How Much Education?

Below is a list of occupations and four different educational levels. Using your career center resources or www.online.onetcenter.org, match the educational requirements of the occupation to the occupational title by drawing a line from the education required to the occupation.

	Petroleum Engineers
	Stock Clerks
High School Diploma	
	Microbiologists
	Agricultural Technicians
Post-secondary Training	**Food Servers**
	Veterinarians
	Photographers
Bachelor's Degree	**Cartoonists**
	Speech-Language Pathologists
	Models
Graduate Degree or Professional Degree	**Lawyers**
	Mathematicians
	File Clerks

Which occupations do you think have the highest salary? _____

_____

_____

Do you think that there is a relationship between education and income?

_____

_____

_____

Online Degrees

More and more academic institutions are offering online degrees. Below is a listing of a few of the degrees you can get using the Internet. For each degree, list the primary interest area of that degree from the options of Realistic, Investigative, Artistic, Social, Enterprising, or Conventional.

Online Degree	Interest Area
Bachelor of Science in Business / Accounting	
Bachelor of Science in Business / Administration	
Bachelor of Science in Business / e-business	
Bachelor of Science in Business / Management	
Bachelor of Science in Business / Marketing	
Bachelor of Science in Criminal Justice Administration	
Bachelor of Science in Human Services / Management	
Bachelor of Science in Information Technology (BSIT)	
Bachelor of Science in Management	
Bachelor of Science in Nursing	
Bachelor's of Business/Accounting	
Bachelor's in Library Science	

Jobs Requiring Less Than a Bachelor's Degree

Below is a listing of the top 10 large-growth and high paying occupations that generally require less training than a bachelor's degree. The information comes from the Bureau of Labor Statistics (www.bls.gov). Identify the occupation according to its primary interest area of Realistic, Investigative, Artistic, Social, Enterprising, or Conventional.

Occupation	Interest Area
Registered nurses	
Truck drivers, heavy and tractor-trailer	
Sales representatives, wholesale and manufacturing, except technical and scientific products	
Maintenance and repair workers, general	
First-line supervisors/managers of retail sales workers	
Electricians	
Computer support specialists	
Police and sheriff's patrol officers	
Licensed practical and licensed vocational nurses	
Executive secretaries and administrative assistants	

Is one interest area represented more than others? _____.

Are some interest areas missing? _____.

High-Growth Jobs Requiring an Associate Degree or Post-secondary Vocational Degree

The Bureau of Labor Statistics has identified the following 10 occupations as the occupations having the most growth in new jobs and that generally require an associate or vocational degree. Categorize the occupations according to their primary interest area of Realistic, Investigative, Artistic, Social, Enterprising, or Conventional.

Occupation	Interest Area
Registered nurses	
Computer support specialists	
Preschool teachers, except special education	
Licensed practical and licensed vocational nurses	
Automotive service technicians and mechanics	
Hairdressers, hairstylists, and cosmetologists	
Fitness trainers and aerobics instructors	
Medical records and health information technicians	
Dental hygienists	
Emergency medical technicians and paramedics	

Is there a category that seems most prevalent? _____.

Are some interest categories missing? _____.

High-Growth Jobs Requiring a Bachelor's Degree

The Bureau of Labor Statistics has identified the following 10 occupations as the occupations having the most growth in new jobs and that generally require a Bachelor's degree. Categorize the occupations according to their primary interest area of Realistic, Investigative, Artistic, Social, Enterprising, or Conventional.

Occupation	Interest Area
Elementary school teachers, except special education	
Accountants and auditors	
Computer systems analysts	
Secondary school teachers, except special and vocational education	
Computer software engineers, applications	
Special education teachers	
Computer software engineers, systems software	
Network systems and data communications analysts	
Network and computer systems administrators	
Computer programmers	

Is there a category that seems most prevalent? _____.

Are any interest categories missing? _____.

High-Growth Jobs Requiring a Graduate Degree

The Bureau of Labor Statistics has identified the following 10 occupations as the occupations having the most growth in new jobs and that generally require a graduate degree. Categorize the occupations according to their primary interest area of Realistic, Investigative, Artistic, Social, Enterprising, or Conventional.

Occupation	Interest Area
Post-secondary teachers	
Lawyers	
Physicians and Surgeons	
Pharmacists	
Clergy	
Physical therapists	
Rehabilitation counselors	
Educational, vocational, and school counselors	
Clinical, counseling, and school psychologists	
Mental health and substance abuse social workers	

Is there a category that seems most prevalent? _____.

Are any interest categories missing? _____.

#57 Educational Requirements

Using your career resources or by using Appendix A, have students list 10 occupations that sound interesting to them. Using information in your career center or from www. online.onetcenter.org, have them list the general educational requirements. Discuss with students how these requirements fit with their current plans. Do some of the occupations have higher educational requirements than initially thought? Do some have less?

#58 Learning Job Skills in Vocational-Technical Schools

Vocational-Technical Schools provide programs that lead directly to important jobs. The following list offers just a sampling of the hundreds of programs that are available: aircraft maintenance technology, audio and recording technology, carpentry, EKG technology, fashion design, hotel and motel management, jewelry design, orthotics, robotics, shipbuilding, welding, surveying and mapping, and so on.

Have the students visit the web site of a vocational-technical school in your geographic area. Have them search the programs that the school has to offer and identify those that relate to their primary interest area. Ask them to prepare a list of school programs that relate to their primary interest area. Discuss with students which programs seem to be most interesting to them.

#59 Learning Job Skills in Community Colleges

Following is a list of some educational programs that are available in community colleges: accounting, animal sciences, child care, cosmetology, dental services, ethnic studies, farm/ranch management industrial arts, foreign languages, computer technologies, food sciences, soil conservation, museum studies, public relations, and so on.

Have your students visit the web site of a community college in your geographic area. Have them identify the programs that the school has to offer that relate to their primary interest area. Discuss what makes the programs of interest to them. Have a discussion about what kinds of jobs they might obtain if they graduate from the program that interests them most. Have them determine if the college has a career center that provides job searching assistance. Ask them to research the kinds of salaries they can expect to receive in the job. Do the salaries that they can anticipate seem to be satisfactory? Are there local jobs that students can obtain after graduating from these programs?

Occupations and Jobs Activities

This section contains the following reproducible student activities:

TITLE	DIRECTIONS
Activity #60 **Occupations**	Distribute a copy of the activity to each student. After completion of the exercise, discuss the answers as a group. See what discrepancies are found. Ask the students to share the occupations that they are interested in. Remember that occupations generally have more than one interest area.
Activity #61 **Tools of the Trade**	Distribute a copy of the activity to each student. After completion of the exercise, discuss the answers as a group. See what discrepancies are found. Some tools can be used by people in several different occupations and interest areas. Have students explain and defend their answers.
Activity #62 **Notable People**	Distribute a copy of the activity to each student. After completion of the exercise, discuss the answers as a group. Although the exercise asks for the primary interest area, be sure to stress that people generally have interests in all six areas, but some are more dominant than others. You may wish to create a new activity using some names more pertinent to your particular clientele. You can also create an exercise that uses only historical figures.

Activity #63 **Making a Hospital Work**	Distribute a copy of the activity to each student. As you discuss the results, see if students can identify other occupations that are involved in hospital work beyond those that are listed. In your discussion with them, be sure to help them conclude that occupations in several interest areas are required to accomplish the task of staffing a hospital.
Activity #64 **Telephone Book**	Distribute a copy of the activity to each student. Discuss that there are a variety of companies in this country and a variety of types of occupations that employ people in all six interest areas. This can be assigned as a homework task so that the student can use their own phonebook.
Activity #65 **Military Enlisted Occupations**	Distribute a copy of the activity to each student. Discuss with your students how civilian and military occupations have tasks that are similar and the skills can transfer from the military to civilian occupations. Be sure to stress that the military has occupations that cut across all six interest areas. Using careersinthemilitary.com, note for your students the various mental and physical requirements of enlisted jobs.
Activity #66 **Military Officer Occupations**	Distribute a copy of the activity to each student. Discuss with your students how civilian and military occupations have tasks that are similar and the skills can transfer from the military to civilian occupations. Be sure to stress that the military has occupations that cut across all six interest areas. Note that officer occupations require higher educational accomplishments than enlisted occupations.

Activity #67 **Self-Employment and Interests**	Distribute a copy of the activity to each student. After students have completed this exercise, work with them to see if there are any trends that you can identify in the types of interest areas that are most and least represented in the 17 occupations that are listed.
Activity #68 **Places to Work**	Distribute a copy of the activity to each student. After the students complete the exercise, be sure to discuss that various occupations have various work environments. Stress also that a variety of different occupations exist in similar workplaces.
Activity #69 **Important Tasks**	Distribute a copy of the activity to each student. Help students locate the onetcenter.org web site and find the tasks section. In discussions with the students, it is important to stress that occupations have a variety of task requirements.
Activity #70 **Internet Job Openings**	Distribute a copy of the activity to each student. You can assign this as a homework activity if you wish. After completion, ask the students to describe their findings. Check to see how their graphs have been crafted. Use the graphing program at http://nces.ed.gov/nceskids/graphing/ if you find it useful. Work with your school's math teacher on this activity.

Activity #71 **Physical Ability/Disability**	Distribute a copy of the activity to each student. After completion of the exercise, discuss the answers as a group. Be sure to stress that employers attempt to provide accommodations so that all individuals can perform their work. Some situations may pose more challenges than others. Discuss the kinds of accommodations that can be made for jobs in each of the six RIASEC areas.
Activity #72 **Flexibility Is the Key**	Distribute a copy of the activity to each student. After completion of the exercise, have students discuss their answers with each other in small groups or as a class discussion. You may wish to review the definition, advantages, and disadvantages of a flexible schedule if you feel it is needed.
Activity #73 **Serve It Up!**	You may wish to precede this activity with a visit to the school cafeteria or a local restaurant. Distribute a copy of the activity to each student. After completion of the exercise, have students discuss their answers with each other in small groups or as a class discussion. In the discussion, you should stress the fact that people of all interest areas are involved in running a business of this nature.

Activity #74 **Job Values**	Distribute a copy of the activity to each student. Before beginning the exercise, stress the fact that people have job values that are important to them and in order for work to be satisfying and fulfilling, most all of the values need to be met. Give some examples of work values that are important to you. After the students complete the activity, discuss their answers provided by your students. Bring out the fact that the same job values can be satisfied in occupations represented by several interest areas. This activity can be very useful in bringing out student perceptions about what is important in their lives and on a job.
Activity #75 **Building Your House**	Distribute a copy of the activity to each student. As you discuss the results, see if students can identify other occupations that are involved in building a house beyond those that are listed. In your discussion, be sure to help them conclude that occupations in several interest areas are required to accomplish the task of building a house.

Occupations

Match the occupation with the interest area. Are the occupations Realistic (R), Investigative (I), Artistic (A), Social (S), Enterprising (E), or Conventional (C)? Put the proper letter next to the activity.

___ **Physicist**

___ **Veterinarian**

___ **Equipment repairer**

___ **Teacher**

___ **Guidance counselor**

___ **Accountant**

___ **Journalist**

___ **Actor/Actress**

___ **Salesperson**

___ **Attorney**

___ **Police officer**

___ **Librarian**

___ **Store manager**

___ **Carpenter**

___ **Archeologist**

___ **Politician**

___ **Cook**

___ **Conductor**

___ **Jazz dancer**

___ **Planetary Scientist**

Circle any occupations that are of interest to you.

List the occupations that are of interest to you and are also in your primary interest area.

_____

_____

_____

Tools of the Trade

Below is a list of tools that might be used by people in various jobs. Match the tool with the major Interest area. Put the proper letter next to the tool – Realistic (I), Investigative (I), Artistic (A), Social (S), Enterprising (E), Conventional (C). Some tools can be used by people in more than one interest area. If this is the case, include all the interest areas.

_____ **Stage**

_____ **Computer**

_____ **Journal**

_____ **Piano**

_____ **Test tube**

_____ **Calculator**

_____ **Paint brush**

_____ **Power drill**

_____ **Ballet shoes**

_____ **Sheet music**

_____ **Thermometer**

_____ **Movie film**

_____ **Camera**

_____ **Farm tools**

_____ **Library cart**

_____ **Ledger**

_____ **Costume**

_____ **Microscope**

_____ **Nursing cap**

With which tools do you think you would enjoy working?

_____

_____

Are you able to use any of these tools in your life now? If so, how?

_____

_____

Notable People

Based on their occupation and activities, guess the primary interest area of the following real, fictitious, or historical people. Match the person with the major interest area. Put the proper letter next to the person. Realistic (R), Investigative (I), Artistic (A), Social (S), Enterprising (E), Conventional (C). Remember, most people have several interest areas, but often one is strongest. If you don't know the person, find out what you can using the Internet.

____ **President G. W. Bush**

____ **President Bill Clinton**

____ **President Jimmy Carter**

____ **Britney Spears**

____ **Tim "the tool man" Taylor**

____ **Donald Trump**

____ **Tiger Woods**

____ **Marie Curie**

____ **Mother Teresa**

____ **Bill Gates**

____ **Oprah Winfrey**

____ **Bob Crachett**

____ **Galileo**

____ **Emeril Lagasse of the Food Network**

____ **Gregor Mendel**

____ **Dr. Phil**

____ **Jennifer Lopez**

Making a Hospital Work

Hospitals perform wondrous deeds because they are filled with employees in many occupations. Below is a list of a few occupations that allow a hospital to function. Indicate the primary interest area of these occupations. Are the occupations Realistic , Investigative, Artistic, Social, Enterprising, or Conventional? Add other occupations and determine their primary interest area.

Interest Area	Occupation
	CEO or Hospital Administrator
	Doctors
	Nurses
	Surgeons
	Lab Technicians
	Nutritionists
	Insurance Processors
	Receptionists
	Emergency Room Technicians
	Food Preparers
	Radiologic Technicians
	Pharmacist
	Physician's Assistant

Do some interest areas appear more frequently than others? Why do think this is so?

_____

_____

Which occupations require a graduate degree? _____

_____

Which occupations require a bachelor's degree? _____

_____

Which occupations require a post-secondary vocational or an associate degree?

_____

_____

Telephone Book

Using the Yellow Pages of a phone book, select three pages at random from three different sections of the phone book. On each of those three pages, pick five listings for a total of 15 listings. Choose companies that also have some advertising in the phone book so that you can read their ads to gather more information about each company. Next to each company you listed indicate the primary interest area of the occupations best represented by that business. For example, **Valley Typesetters** probably employs people who create documents by typing and proofing; these are **Conventional** occupations. Another example would be the company **Entertainment Now**, which provides entertainment for weddings, parties and special events. Entertainers tend to be artistic individuals, so the primary interest area would be **Artistic**.

List your companies and the primary interest area in the space provided below.

	Company	Interest Area
1.		
2.		
3.		
4.		
5.		
6.		
7.		
8.		
9.		
10.		
11.		
12.		
13.		
14.		
15.		

Military Enlisted Occupations

The military provides many good opportunities for job training and career progression. CareersintheMilitary.com provides information on 81 enlisted occupations found in the military. Select two of the occupations below and look them up on the web site under the section titled *enlisted occupations*. Find out what people who are in those occupation do and determine each occupation's primary interest area. List the related civilian occupations. What kind of training is provided in the military for these occupations?

Legal Specialists and Court Reporters
Flight Operations Specialists
Cardiopulmonary and EEG Technicians
Law Enforcement and Security Specialists
Religious Program Specialists
Audiovisual and Broadcast Technicians
Air Traffic Controllers

Occupation 1 _____ Interest Area _____

What People Do in the Occupation _____

_____

Education and Training Provided _____

Related Civilian Occupations _____

_____

Occupation 2 _____ Interest Area _____

What People Do in the Occupation _____

_____

Education and Training Provided _____

Related Civilian Occupations _____

_____

Military Officer Occupations

The U.S. Military identifies 59 officer occupations. A few of these are listed below. Select two of the occupations and look them up on the web site CareersintheMilitary.com. Read what officers in that occupation do and determine the occupation's primary interest area. Find and list the related civilian occupations.

Life Scientists
Helicopter Pilots
Computer Systems Officers
Intelligence Officers
Emergency Management Officers
Speech Therapists
Physicians and Surgeons

Occupation 1 _____ Interest Area _____

What People Do in the Occupation _____

_____

Related Civilian Occupations _____

_____

Occupation 2 _____ Interest Area _____

What People Do in the Occupation _____

_____

Education and Training Provided _____

Related Civilian Occupations _____

_____

Self-Employment and Interest

The Bureau of Labor Statistics has identified the following 17 occupations has having the most self-employed workers. Categorize the occupations by primary interest area of Realistic, Investigative, Artistic, Social, Enterprising, or Conventional. Do you notice any trends? Are some interest areas represented more than others? Are any interest areas missing? Circle the occupations that appeal to you most. Are the occupations you circled in your primary interest area?

Occupation	Interest Area
Farmers and ranchers	
First-line supervisors/managers of retail sales workers	
Child care workers	
Carpenters	
First-line supervisors/managers of non-retail sales workers	
Hairdressers, hairstylists, and cosmetologists	
Landscaping and grounds keeping workers	
Truck drivers, heavy and tractor-trailer	
Painters, construction and maintenance	
Lawyers	
Construction managers	
Real estate sales agents	
Retail salespersons	
Management analysts	
Bookkeeping, accounting, and auditing clerks	
Maids and housekeeping cleaners	
Property, real estate, and community association managers	

Places to Work

All work takes place somewhere and most of us have preferences as to where we like to do our work. Some of us like to work outside, some of us like a nice quiet office, and some of us prefer to work at home. Most occupations have typical locations where the work is performed. For each work setting listed below select at least one occupation that might work at that location and list the primary interest area for that occupation. If you can think of other occupations that work in that setting, but are in another interest area, list that occupation and its interest area as well. For example, many occupations have their primary place of work in an office building like a receptionist, a sales person, and an accountant, but each of these has a different primary interest area.

Work Setting	Occupations	Interest Area(s)
Farm		
State Park		
Automotive Repair Shop		
Stage		
Library		
Under Water		
Hospice Center		
Department Store Sales Floor		
Museum		
Planetarium		
Dance Floor		
Research Ship		
Boeing 747		
Operating Room		
Submarine		

Important Tasks

From the list below, select one of the occupations that might interest you as a future occupation. Write the name of the occupation in the space provided and then list the top three tasks that you would perform if that was your occupation. You can find information about these occupations on http://online.onetcenter.org/.

Electrical Engineers
Fashion Designers
Statisticians
Agricultural Inspectors
Bookkeeping, Accounting, and Auditing Clerks
Flight Attendants
Fitness Trainers and Aerobics Instructors
Commercial Pilots
Public Transportation Inspectors
Public Relations Managers
Astronomers

Occupation	Tasks
	1.
	2.
	3.

Do the tasks seem to relate to your interest areas? _____

After learning about your selected occupation, do you think you would enjoy working in

that field? _____   Why or why not? _____

_____

_____

_____

Internet Job Openings

Go to the web site of a large company that you have seen advertised in the newspaper or on television. Some examples are http://www.hp.com (for Hewlett Packard) or http://www.pg.com (for Proctor and Gamble). Go to the jobs section. Sometimes web sites list this section as **jobs**, **employment**, or **careers**.

In the space below, tally the number of jobs in each interest area and prepare a line graph in the space provided that shows how many jobs are in each interest area. Which category has the most jobs? What conclusions can you draw from this information?

Interest Area	Number of Jobs
Realistic	
Investigative	
Artistic	
Social	
Enterprising	
Conventional	

```
N      55 - ————————————————————————
U
M      50 - ————————————————————————
B
E      45 - ————————————————————————
R
       40 - ————————————————————————

       35 - ————————————————————————

O      30 - ————————————————————————
F
       25 - ————————————————————————

J      20 - ————————————————————————
O
B      15 - ————————————————————————
S
        5 - ————————————————————————

        0 - ————————————————————————
            R    I    A    S    E    C
```

For help in creating a graph, go to the U.S. Department of Education's web site **http://nces.ed.gov/nceskids/graphing/**. This site can help you create various graphs including a bar graph, line graph, pie chart, and area graph.

Physical Ability/Disability

Consider the descriptions of the interest areas listed below and answer the questions regarding which interest area occupations people with disabilities might be especially challenged to perform.

For example, if someone has a visual disability, which interest area or areas would be most difficult to work in? What kinds of accommodations might be implemented to help persons with visual disabilities perform their jobs? What about persons with physical handicaps? What about a person with a hearing impairment?

Realistic   Working with one's hands using tools, machines, equipment, and materials. Preferring to work with animals or in the garden. Best at working with things, as opposed to ideas or people.

Investigative   Working to solve problems. Favorite subjects tend to be science and math related. Like to troubleshoot problems. Like to gather data about a problem and come up with a solution.

Artistic   Tend to be creative. Most favorite activities would involve doing or performing dance, theater, writing, or art.

Social   Like helping people. Very happy to do what can be done to offer help or advice to people who need it. Would like activities such as counseling people or tending to their needs.

Enterprising   Like to lead people to achieve a goal. Want to convince people to do something they don't necessarily want to do. Like to sell ideas or things.

Conventional   Like working with details and numbers. It is important that everything is in order and that certain standards are met and procedures are used.

In which interest areas would someone with a visual disability have the most difficulty?
_____ Find the easiest to work in? _____

What kinds of accommodations might be implemented to help people with visual disabilities perform their job? _____

_____

In which interest areas would someone with a hearing impairment have the most difficulty? _____. Find the easiest to work in? _____

What kind of accommodation might be implemented to help people with hearing impairments perform their job? _____

_____

Flexibility Is the Key

Of the following occupations, which ones might be more likely to have a flexible schedule – that is, a work schedule that differs from day to day or differs from other employees? For example, you might work more hours each work day and have one extra day off per week so that rather than the typical 5-day work week, you work 4 days and have a 3-day weekend. You might start earlier and leave earlier or you might start later and leave later than typical employees.

Indicate whether the occupation is more likely or less likely to have a flexible schedule by checking the appropriate column. Compare your answers with your classmates and discuss your differences.

Occupation	More Likely	Less Likely
Fast Food Cooks		
Welders		
Radio Operators		
Geologists		
Computer Systems Analysts		
Archivists		
Surveyors		
Mathematicians		
Cartoonists		
Curators		
Foreign Language Teachers		
Technical Writers		
Crossing Guards		
Flight Attendants		
Clergy		
Political Science Teachers		
Private Sector Executives		
Real Estate Agents		
Manicurists and Pedicurists		
Housekeeping Supervisors		
File Clerks		
Astronomers		
Tax Preparers		
Computer Operators		

Serve It Up!

You are the owner and operator of a very large and popular restaurant called **Gourmet Corner**. List at least 10 occupations or jobs that are necessary to operate a successful restaurant and identify the primary interest area of each occupation. The interest areas are Realistic, Investigative, Artistic, Social, Enterprising, and Conventional. You may wish to perform some Internet research or visit a local restaurant before you complete this activity.

OCCUPATION   **INTEREST AREA**

1._____   _____

2._____   _____

3._____   _____

4._____   _____

5._____   _____

6._____   _____

7._____   _____

8._____   _____

9._____   _____

10._____   _____

Do certain interest areas seem more frequently represented in this business? If yes, which ones? _____

_____

Do the education levels of these occupations seem to be the same or different?

_____

Rank the jobs in order of the amount of education and training required.

_____

_____

_____

_____

Job Values

Below is a list of job values, things some people believe are important to them in a job. By each value, circle the RIASEC interest area, or areas, that are most likely to include occupations that satisfy that work value. R is Realistic, I is Investigative, A is Artistic, S is Social, E is Enterprising, and C is Conventional. Remember that the job value can be satisfied in occupations in more than one interest area. Select the interest areas that are most likely to satisfy the job value.

For example, the job value of having "friendly and supportive co-workers" can be found in occupations in all six interest areas, but having "high pay" might only be associated with certain enterprising or artistic occupations. Then again, some artistic occupations are associated with low pay.

JOB VALUE

R I A S E C   job security
R I A S E C   good family relations
R I A S E C   international fame and fortune
R I A S E C   a lovely home in a beautiful area
R I A S E C   doing what I want
R I A S E C   excitement and energy
R I A S E C   high pay
R I A S E C   a feeling of accomplishment
R I A S E C   friendly and supportive co-workers
R I A S E C   professional development opportunities
R I A S E C   flexible schedule
R I A S E C   satisfying and useful career

What job values do you think are most directly associated with your primary interest area? _____

_____

Which job values are most important to you at this point in time? _____

_____

Do you think your job values will change at some later time? _____

How might your job values be different 15 years from now? _____

_____

Building Your House

Building a house requires the skills of many types of occupations including architects, general contractors, framers, plumbers, carpenters, order clerks, structural engineers, landscape architects, bankers, designers and decorators, carpet installers, painters, electricians, and code inspectors.

Determine and then list the primary interest area of each of these occupations in the space provided. The interest areas are Realistic, Investigative, Artistic, Social, Enterprising, and Conventional.

Interest Area	Occupation
	Architects
	General Contractors
	Framers
	Plumbers
	Carpenters
	Order Clerks
	Structural Engineers
	Landscape Architects
	Bankers
	Designers and Decorators
	Carpet Installers
	Painters
	Electricians
	Code Inspectors

What conclusions can you draw from the variety of interest areas listed?

_____

_____

#76 Buddy Business

Suggest to your students that they interview a friend or family member about the job that he or she has. Students should ask what is done on the job and why that occupation was chosen. Students should also ask what the person likes or doesn't like about the job. During the interview students need to determine whether or not the person is happy with the kind of work he or she is doing.

Have the students identify the interest area of the occupation. If it is necessary they can go to http://online.onetcenter.org/ in order to identify the interest area. (This can be done by clicking on the "Find Occupations" section, entering the name of the person's occupation in the space provided, and locating the interest area in the "Summary Reports" section of the web site.)

Have students determine whether or not these interest areas are the same or different from the interest areas of their family member or friend. (If they are not aware of the person's interest area, students can ask the person to complete one of the checklists found in the Measuring Interests section of this chapter.)

Generally, people who are in an occupation that has the same interest area as their personal interest areas tend to be more satisfied with their work. Discuss with the students if this is true in the case of their family member or friend. If he or she is not satisfied with the occupation, ask the student to speculate the reasons. Have the students determine if the dissatisfaction has to do with the occupation or with some factor about the work being done—like his or her boss, schedule, pay, co-workers, the travel time, etc.

Work with the students to draw conclusions about interests and occupations from this exercise.

#77 Non-Traditional Occupations

Jobs in some occupations tend to be filled predominantly by either males or females. For example, carpenters and construction workers are generally male. Nurses and elementary school teachers are generally female.

Have your students interview a person working in a non-traditional occupation. Ask them to write a story that describes that person's decision-making process about why and how he or she decided to go into the field. For example, the students might interview a female scientist or astronaut or a male early childhood teacher. Have the students ask the following questions: What made you decide to enter the field? What challenges or problems did you have to face in order to qualify for the job? What advice do you have for others who might want to enter a non-traditional field? Ask the students to determine whether the person's primary interest area matches the work being done. Have the students share their stories with each other.

#78 Unusual Occupations

Select at least six of the occupations listed below and write them on the board. Have your students go to your career center or www.onlineonetcenter.org to determine the primary interest area of the occupations you have selected:

Amusement and Recreation Attendants
Dot Etchers
Coroners
Caption Writers
Shoe and Leather Workers and Repairers
Animal Control Workers
Self-Enrichment Education Teachers
Locker Room Attendants
Sales Engineers
Directory Assistance Operators
Marking Clerks
Job Printers

Next ask the students to determine the education levels, primary tasks, and important skills of each occupation.

Engage the students in a discussion that involves the educational requirements of these occupations. Have them discuss how many people might be employed in each of these occupations on a national level. Which of these occupations generally offer high pay? Do any of these occupations offer a flexible schedule? Where would one get training for these occupations?

#79 Visiting a Company

Make arrangements for small teams of your students (about three) to visit a company or organization in your town. You will need to make arrangements with the company representative and explain the intent of this activity. It would be best if all your students did not visit the same company.

Ask each student to talk with three people in that company or organization and watch what they do during the day. Have the students ask and record the answers to the following questions: Why did they take this job? Do they like what they are doing? What are the tasks they perform? With whom do they interact? What tools do they use?

Have the students determine the primary interest areas by having each person complete one of the interest checklists found in the *Measuring Interests* section of this chapter. Ask the students to determine if the person's interest area is the same as the occupation's interest area. If there is a mismatch between the person and the occupation, ask the students to find out what attracted the person to the occupation. Is it the schedule? the money? the location?

After the visits, discuss the results and ask the students what they learned. Are the people happy and excited about what they are doing? Do they intend on staying in the job for a long time or are they looking for something different? Be sure to ask the students what they learned from the experience.

#80 Homework

Using your career center or the Internet, have students identify 15 occupations in their primary interest area and discuss how all or parts of the occupational requirements could be performed from home rather than at the traditional workplace.

Have the students discuss what kind of equipment they would need at home to perform the job. Ask the students to discuss what types of distractions they might have if they worked from home.

#81 Day-to-Day Activities

Have your students select one of the following occupations and write about a typical day in the life of a person working in the chosen occupation. Ask the students to include some specifics about the person's schedule, the tools that would be used, the people he or she would meet and talk to, what would be worn, what the person has to read on the job, etc. The student should determine the occupation's primary interest area. To perform this task students should either interview a person in that occupation or research the occupation from materials in your career center or on the Internet.

Biologist

Ship Captain

Taxi Driver

Prosecuting Attorney

Librarian

Jeweler

Mechanic

Grocery Clerk

Magazine Editor

Brick Layer

Playwright

Criminologist

Human Resource Specialist

Telemarketer

Stock Broker

Ask the students why they selected the occupation they did. Have the student compare with at least two other students what they wrote and consider the following questions:. Are the day-to-day activities for these occupations similar or very different? Do the occupations the students selected have flexible or rigid schedules? Which occupations have the highest pay? Which occupations will generally interact more with people on a day-to-day basis?

#82 Indoors, Outdoors, or Both

Using information in your career center or on www.online.onetcenter.org, have the students identify 10 different occupations in their interest area. They should examine the descriptions of the occupations and predict which occupations might generally be performed indoors, outdoors, or both. Discuss with the students what their own preferences are – indoors, outdoors, or both?

#83 Not Me!

Ask the students to identify an occupation that they would never want to have and then determine what it is that makes them dislike this occupation. Ask why they don't like those features of the occupation. Discuss with them the following questions: Does the occupation have requirements you are not good at? Could you learn them? Do you want to learn them? What aspects of the occupation do you prefer to avoid?

#84 Salary

Using Appendix A or information in your career center, have the students pick five occupations in their major interest area, determine what the average salary is for the occupations, and rank them from lowest to highest salary. Have the students answer the following questions: How much does salary mean to you? Is salary more important than working in a job you love? Is salary more important than a job that is making a difference in society? Is it more important than having compatible co-workers?

#85 Physical Requirements

Using Appendix A or information in your career center, have your students pick five occupations in their major interest area. Have students research what physical capabilities are required for those occupations. Discuss the following questions: Are those physical requirements reasonable for you? If you had a physical disability, what type of accommodation could be implemented that would allow you to perform the job regardless of the physical challenge?

#86 The Shadow Knows

Make arrangements for each student to shadow a person in an occupation that matches the student's primary interest area or an occupation that you know the students might like to learn more about.

After the shadowing experience, ask the students whether the person they shadowed was performing tasks that they expected. If not, what was unanticipated? Did the students determine that the occupation they observed might be a possible occupation for them to pursue? If they have rejected the occupation, determine what aspects of the occupation caused them to make that decision.

#87 Reverse Interview

Have your students select an occupation in their primary interest area. Have them develop interview questions that might be asked of them as they interview for a job in their selected occupation. Ask the students to prepare answers to those questions, as well.

Have the students exchange their questions with a partner and ask those questions of each other. Ask the students to consider the following questions as they listen to their partners respond to the interview questions: How plausible were the answers? Were the right questions asked? Did the questions relate to qualifications or to other factors?

#88 Using the Internet to Gather Information

There is a lot of good information on the Internet about occupations and their characteristics. Have the students find out about the interest areas of various occupations. Here is one good way to do it.

Go to http://online.onetcenter.org/

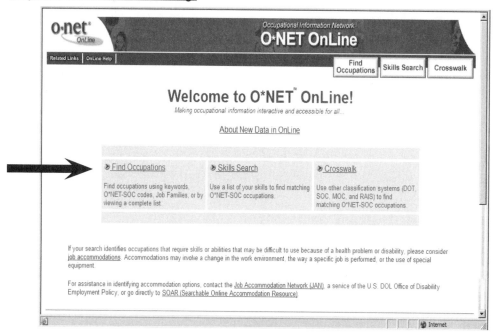

Click on "Find Occupations" and enter one of the following:

Electrical Engineers   **Flight Attendants**
Fashion Designers   **Commercial Pilots**
Statisticians   **Agricultural Inspectors**
Astronomers   **Public Relations Managers**
Bookkeeping, Accounting,   **Fitness Trainers**
**   and Auditing Clerks**   **   and Aerobics Instructors**

Have the students go to the "Summary Reports" section and then click on interests to find the primary interest areas of the occupation. Have them enter other occupations that they want to explore.

Ask the students to list the tasks that a person in this occupation needs to have, and how much education is needed to work in this occupation

#89 Your Job in the Future

Have the students go to the Bureau of Labor Statistics web site at http://www.bls.gov/oco/ to find the *Occupational Outlook Handbook*. Have them select an occupation that is of interest to them and use the search function on the web site to locate information on the occupation.

Click to search

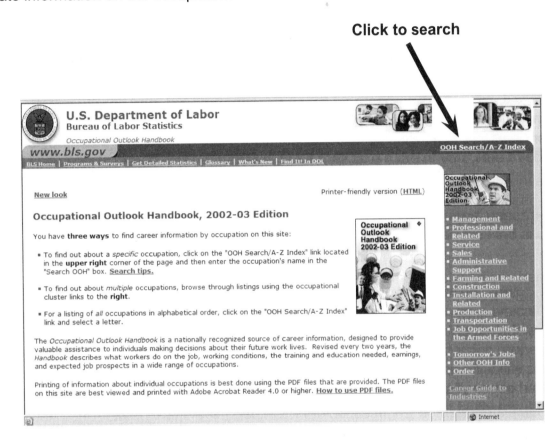

(continued next page)

They should enter the name of the occupation in the space provided. The web site will provide information on that occupation.

Enter name of occupation

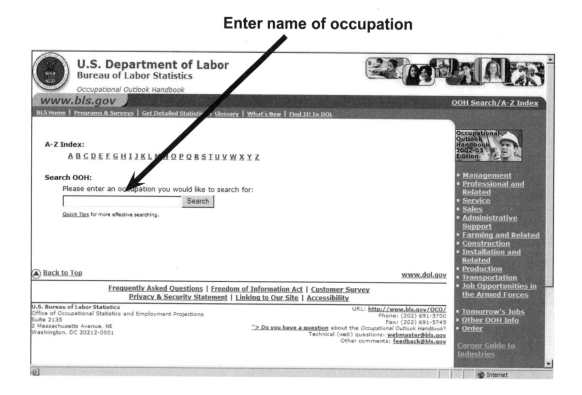

Ask students to answer the following questions based on the occupation that is of most interest to them at the present time.
- Is the occupation growing in its importance in U.S. and global economy or is it dwindling in importance?
- What is the projected outlook for this occupation?
- Is the projected need for this occupation growing at an average rate, growing faster than average, growing slower than average, or not growing much at all?

Discuss with the students whether their occupation of choice seems to be a good fit for the future. Work with the students to determine if they are likely to find a job in their occupation of choice when they complete the necessary education and training. How can they use the same skills needed in their occupation of choice in other occupations in the future? Are there any transferable skills?

#90 Related Occupations

Ask your students to select an occupation in their primary interest area and check it out in the *Occupational Outlook Handbook* at http://www.bls.gov/oco/. Once they have retrieved information on their occupations, have them go to the section called Related Occupations. This will show students that there are occupations with similar skills and tasks to the one they have selected.

Have students determine the answers to the following questions:
- What are some related occupations to the one you selected?
- Are these occupations in the same primary interest area as the one you selected?
- What characteristics seem to make these occupations similar to the original one you selected?

Related Occupations

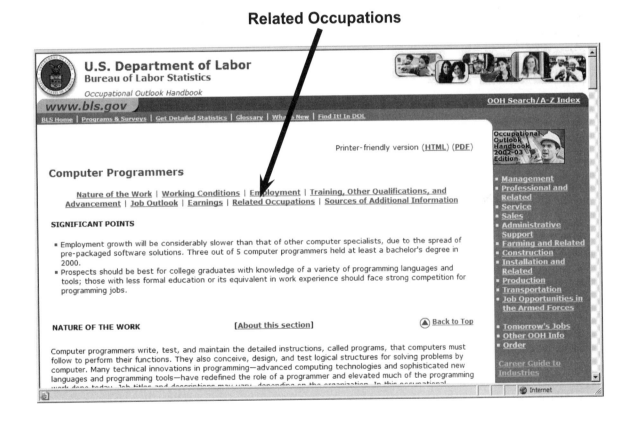

#91 Finding Out More

Many occupations have professional and trade organizations that support and promote them. Examples include the American Federation of Teachers, the Visiting Nurses Association, etc. These organizations are sources of additional information about an occupation, its requirements, apprenticeships, training opportunities, and licensing requirements. The purpose of this activity is to help students understand where they can obtain additional information. This information can come from looking at a web site or by writing the association for supplemental information.

Have students check out the *Occupational Outlook Handbook* at http://www.bls.gov/oco/ or use the information in your career center. On the Occupational Outlook Handbook web site, they should first search for their occupation of interest and then click on Sources of Additional Information.

Students should indicate to you what their sources of information are. Suggest that they visit the relevant web sites or write to the organization for further information. Ask the students if there were any surprises in what they discovered.

Sources of Additional Information

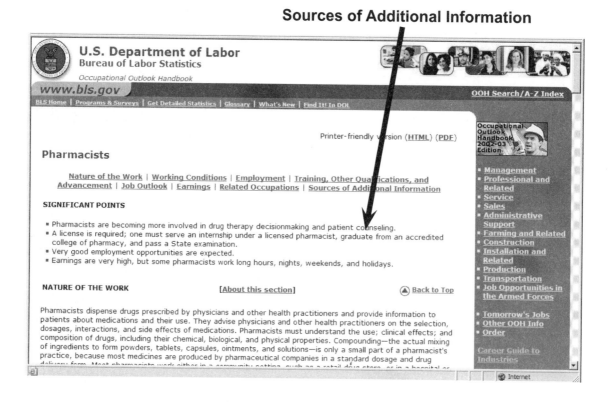

Have the students contact one of the organizations that relate to the occupation of interest. What type of information can this organization provide?

#92 Occupations in a Career Cluster

Sometimes a good way to think about occupations is in groupings called occupational clusters. The Occupational Outlook Handbook provides that opportunity. Go to the online version of the Occupational Outlook Handbook at http://www.bls.gov/oco/ and have your students select one of the occupational clusters. The clusters include Management, Professional and Related, Service, Sales, Administrative Support, Farming and Related, Construction, Installation and Related, Production, and Transportation

Ask students to examine the occupations in one of those clusters and identify two occupations in that cluster for each of the six RIASEC interest areas. For example, if the student selects the Service cluster, have them identify two Realistic occupations, two Investigative occupations, two Artistic occupations, two Social occupations, two Enterprising occupations, and two Conventional occupations.

Have a discussion with the students to determine if it was difficult to find occupations for each of the six interest areas. Did any of your students determine that the occupations in the cluster they selected were predominantly in one or several interest areas? For example, they might find that occupations in the Construction cluster were mostly in the Realistic interest area.

Occupational Cluster

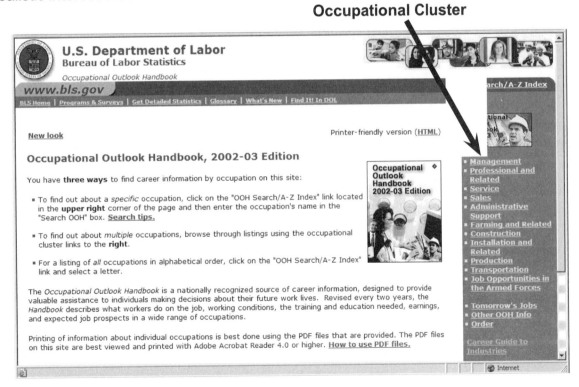

#93 Hottest Jobs

The Bureau of Labor Statistics identifies the following occupations as the ten fastest growing occupations for the next several years. List the occupations on the blackboard. Ask the students to identify the primary interest area for each of the occupations. If necessary they should use the resources in your career center or go to http://online.onetcenter.org to assist them. Have a discussion about the training and education requirements for each occupation.

> Medical Assistants
> Network Systems and Data Communications Analysts
> Physician Assistants
> Social and Human Service Assistants
> Home Health Aides
> Medical Records and Health Information Technicians
> Physical Therapist Aides
> Computer Software Engineers, Applications
> Computer Software Engineers, Systems Software
> Physical Therapist Assistants

Ask the students why they think these occupations are currently the hottest jobs in the U.S. economy. What are the factors that might cause these occupations to be so important?

Have the students examine these occupations and decide whether the hottest jobs are distributed across all six interest areas or focused on a few interest areas. Which interest areas seem to represent the hottest jobs? Which interest areas seem to be missing from this list? Ask students how their own primary interest areas match with the interest areas represented by these hottest jobs.

#94 Shrinking Jobs

The Bureau of Labor Statistics identifies the following occupations as the ones projected to be losing the most jobs over the next several years. Fewer jobs will be available in these occupations as the need for these occupations is diminishing. Read each occupation to the student or write the list on the blackboard. Have the students determine the primary interest area of each occupation. Have them use http://online. onetcenter.org or other resources, if necessary, to assist them in determining the primary interest area.

Farmers and Ranchers
Sewing Machine Operators
Word Processors and Typists
Stock Clerks and Order Fillers
Secretaries, Except Legal, Medical and Executive
Electrical and Electronic Equipment Assemblers
Computer Operators
Telephone Operators
Postal Service Mail Sorters, Processors, and Processing Machine Operators
Loan Interviewers and Clerks

Have a discussion about the interest areas most represented by the occupations on this list. Ask the students if they detect any trends. What are the education requirements of these occupations? Are there any conclusions that can be drawn from examining the educational requirements and training requirements of these occupations? Ask them if they think these occupations have lower educational and training requirements or higher educational requirements. Ask them to postulate what factors in the U.S. economy might have changed the need for workers in these occupations. Speculate with them as to whether or not the proliferation of technology had a role.

#95 Robots

Robots are starting to perform some jobs in the U.S. economy. Have the students name occupations in each interest area that can be performed by robots or at least assisted by them. The students may need to do some library or Internet research to learn about robots and what they do.

Ask your students which occupations they think will most likely be automated in the future? What are the education requirements of these occupations. Can they predict how their lives might be affected in the future with more robotic workers?

#96 Cruising Along

Have the students pretend that they are the captains of a passenger cruise ship called *Fantastico* that will launch on its first voyage in three months. It has 300 sleeping rooms, a sun deck, three restaurants, an entertainment center, a fitness center, a beauty and barber shop, a gift shop, a doctor's office, and child care center. Before the first sailing, the captain needs to hire a full crew.

Have your students work in teams of three to create a list of the jobs that the ship will need. Be sure that they don't forget the people who steer the ship! Once they have completed the list, have them identify the occupation's primary interest area of each job.

Ask your students what interest areas are most represented in the ship's crew. Is one interest area represented by more jobs than others? Is it necessary to have occupations from all six interest areas? What job would you prefer on this ship?

#97 Crafting Your Ideal Job

Have the students take some time to think about their ideal job. Have them write a few paragraphs describing what they would like to be doing, where they would be doing it, how much money they will make, where they will live, how they will dress, with whom they will work, what equipment they will use, how they will feel when they perform the job and how it relates to their primary interest area.

Have the students share their writing with someone they admire and that they think gives good advice. A good choice would be one of their parents, another relative, a teacher, or a mentor. Have the students discuss with that person what they think about their concept of their ideal job. Does the person think it is realistic, unrealistic, impossible, possible? On what basis do they form that opinion?

Discuss with students what they learned from the discussion. Did the discussion verify their thoughts or did it make them question what they were thinking? How was their thinking modified?

Career Planning

This section contains the following reproducible student activities:

TITLE	DIRECTIONS
Activity #98 **My Career Plan – Elementary Grades**	Provide a copy of the career plan to each student. If you feel that the activity should be modified in some way to better suit your audience, you may wish to retype and modify it to suite your needs and those of your students. Work with young children to have them think about what they are interested in and what courses they want and have to take in the future. Provide assistance to students to help them complete the plan. Have the students share their plan with parents or guardians.
Activity #99 **My Career Plan – Middle School**	Make a copy of the career plan for each student. If you feel that the activity should be modified in some way to better suit your audience, you may wish to retype and modify it to suit your needs and those of your students. Have them complete the plan and assist them as they work on it. At this stage the emphasis should be on high school courses as well as occupations. Work with students to complete the plan. Have the students share the plan with parents or guardians.

Activity #100 **My Career Plan – High School**	Provide a copy of the career plan to each student. If you feel that the activity should be modified in some way to better suit your audience, you may wish to retype and modify it to suit your needs and those of your students. Have them complete the plan. Focus on this stage should be on post-secondary education, job training, occupational choices and preparation for the future. Work with students to complete the plan. Have the students share the plan with parents or guardians.
Activity #101 **My Career Plan – Post-secondary**	Provide a copy of the plan to high school graduates and adults. If you feel that the activity should be modified in some way to better suit your audience, you may wish to retype and modify it to suit your needs and those of your students. Focus in this stage should be on further education, preparation for occupation, and job preparation. Work with individuals to complete the plan.

My Career Plan – Elementary Grades

I. My Information

Name: _____ Grade Level: _____

School Name: _____ School Counselor or Teacher: _____

II. Here's What I Want People to Know About Me

My Interests	
My Hobbies	
What I am Good At	
This Is What Makes Me Special	
These Are Things I Want to Improve	

III. These Are My Goals

Goals *(What I want to be or what I want to do in the future)*	Courses I Need to Take to Reach My Goals

IV. Things I Have Experienced

School Experiences *(List special experience and opportunities you have had in school, like clubs, awards, recognitions, etc.)*

Activity	Date

V. Draw a Picture of What You Enjoy Doing

When you have completed the plan, sign and date the document and have a counselor, teacher, or mentor review your plan and sign, as well.

Student Signature: _____ **Date:** _____

Counselor/Teacher Signature _____**Date:** _____

My Career Plan – Middle School

I. My Personal Data

Name: _____ Grade Level: _____

School Name: _____ School Counselor/Teacher: _____

II. About Me

My Interests	
My Hobbies	
My Abilities	
My Special Qualities	
Areas I Would Like to Improve or Strengthen	

III. These are My Goals

| Goals

(What I want to be or do in the future.) | Action Steps

(What I need to do to get there.) | Education Plan

(Courses I will need to take in high school.) |
|---|---|---|
| | | |

IV. What I Need to Be Successful at Reaching My Goals

O Tutoring in _____

O Find a Mentor

O Get Help in Organizing My Time

O Take a Course in _____

O Other _____

O Learn Better Study Skills

O Join a Support Group

O Find a Quiet Place to Study

O Improve Test-Taking Skills

V. My Plans After I Graduate High School

O Four-Year College or University

O Work in a Job

O Military Service

O Community or Junior College

O Technical or Trade School

O National Service

VI. What I Want My Counselor or Teacher to Know About Me

When you have completed the plan, sign and date the document and have a counselor, teacher, or mentor review your plan and sign, as well.

Student Signature: _____ Date: _____

Counselor/Teacher/Mentor Signature _____Date: _____

My Career Plan – High School

I. My Personal Data

Name: _____ Grade Level: _____

School Name: _____ School Counselor: _____

II. About Me

My Interests	
My Hobbies	
My Abilities	
My Special Qualities	
My Special Achievements	
Areas I Would Like to Improve or Strengthen	
My Dream Job	

III. These Are My Future Goals

Goals *(What I want to be or do in the future.)*	Action Steps *(What I need to do to get there.)*	Education and Training Plan *(What kind of courses I need to take, what kind of education I need and what training I need to take.)*

IV. Things I Have Experienced

School Experiences *(List special experience and opportunities you have had in school, like clubs, awards, recognitions, etc.)*

Activity	Date

Work Experiences *(Jobs you have had, paid or unpaid.)*

Activity	Date

Volunteer Service *(Special experience and opportunities you have had in serving the community or doing organized service work.)*

Activity	Date

V. Evidence of Other Capabilities I Possess *(Evidence of experiences you have showing the following skills)*

Skills	Experiences
Basic Skills: I can listen to, read, and analyze the ideas of others, use information from a variety of sources and apply mathematical operations to solve problems orally or in writing.	
Thinking Skills: I can evaluate facts, solve advanced problems, and make decisions using logic and reasoning skills.	
Personal Qualities: I can demonstrate an ability to respect others and work as a member of a team.	
Interpersonal Skills: I can demonstrate an ability to work with others, present facts that support arguments, listen to different points of view, and engage in a collaborative decision-making process.	
Technology: I can select and use appropriate technology to complete a task.	
Managing Information: I can select and communicate information in an appropriate format (e.g., oral, written, graphic, multimedia).	
Managing Resources: I know how to access the financial, human, and material resources needed to accomplish tasks and activities.	
Systems: I can understand how to work with changing systems in an organization.	

Family Resources/Family View of Work: I can understand the value of work and the resources needed to help me accomplish my career plan.	
Stereotyping/Non-Traditional: I can understand the opportunities available for entry into nontraditional careers.	

VI. My Goals After High School

O Four-Year College or University   O Community or Junior College
O Work in a Job   O Technical or Trade School
O Military Service   O National Service
O Other

VII. Occupations I Have Explored

Occupation	Positives	Negatives
1.		
2.		
3.		
4.		
5.		

VIII. My Action Steps *(What I need to do next to attain my goals)*

1.

2.

3.

4.

5.

IX. References (List persons who will write letters of reference and support for you.)

When you have completed the plan, sign and date the document and have a counselor, teacher, or mentor review your plan and sign, as well.

Student Signature: _____ **Date:** _____

Counselor/Teacher/Mentor Signature _____**Date:** _____

My Career Plan – Post-secondary

I. My Personal Data

Name: _____ Date: _____

II. About Me

My Interests	
My Hobbies	
My Abilities	
My Special Qualities	
My Special Achievements	
Areas I Would Like to Improve or Strengthen	

III. My Goals – Five Years from Now

Goals (What I want to be or do in the future.)	Action Steps (What I need to do to get there.)	Education and Training Plan (What kind of courses I need to take, what kind of education I need, and what training I need to take.)

IV. Things I Have Experienced

School Experiences. (*List special experience and opportunities you have had in school, like clubs, awards, recognitions, etc.*)

Activity	Date

Work Experiences *(List all work experience you have had, either paid or unpaid.)*

Activity	Date

Volunteer Experiences *(List special experiences and community services.)*

Activity	Date

V. Evidence of Other Capabilities I Possess *(Evidence of experiences you have showing the following skills.)*

Skills	Experiences
Basic Skills: I can listen to, read, and analyze the ideas of others, use information from a variety of sources and apply mathematical operations to solve problems orally or in writing.	
Thinking Skills: I can evaluate facts, solve advanced problems, and make decisions using logic and reasoning skills.	
Personal Qualities: I can demonstrate an ability to respect others and work as a member of a team.	
Interpersonal Skills: I can demonstrate an ability to work with others, present facts that support arguments, listen to different points of view, and engage in a collaborative decision-making process.	
Technology: I can select and use appropriate technology to complete a task.	
Managing Information: I can select and communicate information in an appropriate format (e.g., oral, written, graphic, multimedia).	
Managing Resources: I know how to access the financial, human, and material resources needed to accomplish tasks and activities.	
Systems: I can understand how to work with changing systems in an organization.	

Family Resources/Family View of Work: I can understand the value of work and the resources needed to help me accomplish my career plan.	
Stereotyping/Non-Traditional: I can understand the opportunities available for entry into nontraditional careers.	

VI. Occupations I Have Explored

Occupation	Positives	Negatives
1.		
2.		
3.		
4.		
5.		

VII. What I Have Done to Prepare for a Job

O Prepared a Resume

O Practiced Interview Skills

O Interviewed People in My Job of Interest

O Shadowed People in My Job of Interest

O Read About the Job Requirements

O Learned About the Future Outlook for This Occupation

O Learned About the Skills Needed for This Occupation

O Learned About the Typical Salary for This Occupation

O Know What Training I Need to Perform the Job Well

O Know How the Occupation Satisfies My Interest Areas

O Identified How My Abilities Relate to the Occupation

VIII. My Action Steps *(What I need to do next to pursue my goals.)*

1.

2.

3.

4.

5.

IX. References *(List persons who will write letters of reference and support for you.)*

Chapter 3:

Selecting and Using the
Right Inventory for Your Students and Clients

In the next chapter, information on the various RIASEC-based interest inventories from which to choose for use with your students or clients is provided. You have many options. It is important to remember that the information in that chapter originates from the publishers themselves. With all of these possible choices, how can you sort through the information and decide which instrument is most appropriate for your use, if any?

Deciding may not be easy, but there are several factors to bear in mind during your decision-making process. These are listed and described in this chapter. Each of these factors should be considered before selecting an instrument for your use.

Match Your Purpose with the Instrument's Purpose: First determine the purpose or reason why you are administering the assessment. Is it to conduct preliminary discussions about interest areas? Is it for basic career exploration? Is it to identify a range of occupations or a few specific ones? Is it for selecting a college major or training program? Might it be for job selection? Which inventory seems to fit your purpose best? State your purpose in very clear terms and compare that information to what the publisher says that their instrument is best suited to deliver. Your purpose should match the capability of the instrument and its stated purpose.

Compare Inventory Characteristics and the Audience: The instrument you select should fit the characteristics of the person or persons who will actually take the instrument. More specifically, an assessment should have directions and items that can be understood by the same age or grade level of your students or clients. As an example, an interest inventory developed for adults in transition is likely not to be appropriate for a middle school or high school student.

Do the items have content that is easily understood by your students or clients? Does the assessment use vocabulary that is familiar to your students or clients? If you serve minority or racially diverse clientele, are the words, phrases, or statements likely to be comfortable to and suitable for those individuals? Do the statements match the experiences of those special groups? Do the items resonate with both males and females?

Interest inventories often have lists of activities and occupations; do they have meaning and relevance to the audience you are serving? Some inventories are designed, at least in part, to assist people in selecting a college major. Does this matter to your clientele?

Study the Development Procedures and Norms: Good assessments are based on developmental procedures that involve gathering data on students or clients with characteristics similar to the intended target audience of the assessment. For example, an assessment that is designed for middle school students should be developed through item tryouts with a broad range of middle school students.

Many interest inventories have what are called norms. For your purposes, it is important that the norms have been obtained by assessing a representative sample of individuals similar to your students or clients. It is to this norm group that your students' or clients' results may be compared. Relevant characteristics are age, gender, racial and ethnic group, and socio-economic status. Read the publisher's technical information to make that determination. Decide how close the developmental and norm group is to the groups that will use this instrument. They should correspond closely.

Review Format and Delivery: If there is an option of taking the assessment on paper, via the computer, or over the Internet, be sure that the format and delivery platform do not influence the outcome of the results.

Will you offer your students or clients an option of assessment platform? If so, you need to be sure that there is evidence showing that the results on a paper/pencil instrument will be the same as the results delivered via computer or over the Internet. Comparability of assessment results is a very important concept, as not all assessments give the same results or level of reporting. If they offer multiple delivery platforms and/ or formats, publishers need to conduct research and show evidence of the degree of comparability.

Do you or your students prefer a paper/pencil assessment or one delivered via the computer or administered via the Internet? Some research shows that students prefer a computer format for taking an assessment; some older individuals and some ethnic groups may not be so inclined.

Assessment takers should not be intimidated by the format of the instrument; rather, they should be concentrating on answering the items to the best of their ability. Directions and format should be easy to follow regardless of the delivery platform. Navigation should be simple and intuitive. If your students or clients have not had much exposure to computer assessments, the inventory should provide opportunities for individuals to practice navigating through the assessment, answering items, changing answers, and submitting their final selections. Are such opportunities included in the interest inventory of your choice? Are the directions clear to your target audience?

Decide About the Scoring Process: A key factor to be considered in the selection of an assessment is the scoring process. Scoring can be performed by the person taking the assessment, by you as the user, or automatically by a scoring program.

Some instruments provide a self-scoring option. One consideration in self-scoring is the complexity of the scoring process. The more difficult and complicated the process, the more likely that errors in scoring will be made, leading to incorrect outcomes and interpretations. Simple functions such as counting or adding have been shown to pose fewer problems than scoring procedures which require the transposition of information from one page to another and/or multi-stage processes that include multiplication, division, or weighting of responses in any way. Think about self-scoring requirements versus the capabilities of your students or clients.

If the instrument is not self-scored, will you need to score the inventory yourself? If you have just a few completed instruments, scoring them may not be too onerous; but a classroom full of inventories may require a significant amount of time. The more complicated the scoring procedures, the more open the process is to error and interpretation problems.

Perhaps the responses to the items are placed on a scannable sheet for scoring by the instrument's publisher or an external vendor. This technique enhances accuracy, but some additional factors must be considered. If scanning answer sheets is an option, you may wish to weigh the benefits of accurate scoring against the degree of delay in receiving the results back in sufficient time to be of use to your students or clients. It may be worth it to purchase or lease a scanner and a scoring program if you have many instruments to score and do it frequently.

Scoring of online assessments generally offers the best of both worlds – accuracy and quick turnaround. However, with this option, privacy and security may be issues.

Review How Results Are Reported: Look at the kind of information that is returned to the student or client. Sometimes the kind and amount of information that is provided differs based on whether the instrument is delivered via paper/pencil, by computer, or by Internet. Some of these differences may be important to you. Do not presume that just because the paper/pencil instrument you have used for many years supplies certain results, that the computer version will do the same.

Review the scoring procedures and resulting output to determine whether it is sufficient for your intentions and for the needs of your students and clients. Be sure to look at the options and make your selection based on the kind of results that will be reported.

When using a computer or Internet delivery, results are usually provided instantaneously so they may be discussed immediately. Immediate and positive feedback is generally interesting, meaningful, and stimulating to the assessment taker.

Consider how the student or client will receive a copy of the results. Does the publisher provide results via mail, email, or Internet?

Another important aspect of reporting is the amount of information provided. Systems that are paper-based and self-scored often provide only minimal or basic information. Automated systems often report larger amounts of information tailored to the assessment taker. Look at the score reports to determine what information is provided and how that compares to how you and your students or clients wish to use the information. The amount of information must be right for the age and level of readiness of the persons with whom you are working. It is possible that too much information will overwhelm the assessment takers and prevent them from moving forward in their career development or life planning. Too little information is not very helpful either. These are judgment calls you should make based on knowldege of your audience.

Determine the Clarity and Validity of the Interpretation: It is to the assessment taker's benefit if results are accompanied by accurate, supportable, and clear interpretations. Clarity and validity of interpretations should be a prime consideration in the selection of a good assessment.

Assessment results need to be understood by your students or clients in order to be useful. Determine whether or not the results are provided in a form that makes sense and is helpful to your students or clients.

Sometimes graphical or pictorial representations are the quickest to understand and interpret, but they may gloss over more comprehensive descriptions. Other assessments may provide enormous amounts of information to the point of overload and over-interpretation, often confusing or paralyzing the person from taking reasonable action or making informed decisions. You may see marketing information about some assessments that brag about providing dozens of pages of interpretive information, seducing you into thinking that more is better.

You should judge whether or not the results and the interpretation are sufficient to help the individual understand the outcomes and appropriate action that might be taken using those results. Another good way of deciding how helpful the interpretation is would be to ask your students or clients what they think! Do they agree that the information is helpful to them?

Clear interpretations are not the only criterion. Investigate whether or not the interpretations are supported by research. The publisher should provide evidence that the interpretations being reported to the assessment taker are backed up by evidence. Generally, this evidence can be found in the technical manual or by asking the publisher's representative. It is also important that the results are interpreted only when evidence to do so has been provided. Assessment developers may indicate how the results should not be used and it is important to follow their recommendation on that point.

Decide About Saving and Storing Results: You need to decide if you want to keep the results/scores from the interest inventory and, if so, how you will keep the results. Will you use the assessment results just once and provide the results only to the students or your clients, or will you want to keep the results for future reference? Will you want the students or clients to be able to save and retrieve their results? Think through this issue as it may impact your decision on which assessment to use and how it should be delivered.

If you wish to keep the results of a paper/pencil instrument for future reference, you may want to keep records of the students' scores by transcribing them into a paper system or into a separate database. If you select a computer-delivered assessment, be sure that the scores are automatically saved on the computer or computer network in some defined record keeping system. Otherwise, you will need to keep a separate paper filing system or create an electronic file of your own.

The same considerations apply to an assessment that is delivered and scored online. Will the scores need to be recorded separately in your own filing and storage system or will the results be stored on a publisher's server for access at a later point in time? If results are saved on the publisher's server, are you able to download the information when you want it? How secure is the information and who has access to the results? How long will the results be kept? Will the students or clients have access to their information?

Perhaps you will use an assessment tool that is on a stand-alone computer. Often, in order to protect a person's privacy, many assessments offered on stand-alone computers do not permit saving a person's results because others may easily access the information. You may need to devise another way of saving the results.

Some computer programs save the results and other usage information, such as how many times persons used the program, how long they spent in the program, whether they took the inventory before and how many times, and what parts of the program were most visited. If this information is important to you, be sure to investigate whether or not the publisher provides that capability.

If you want to keep assessment results electronically, such as in a database, it would be very wise to consult with your school's or district's technology experts to assure that you can obtain and retrieve the information that you want.

Obtain Further Published Information: Once you've narrowed down your options to two or three instruments, be sure to obtain the user's guide and technical report from the publisher for each of the instruments you are seriously considering. Read these documents carefully to be sure that the instrument has the characteristics that you want. Has the research in developing the instrument been done on individuals who are like your students? Is the reliability of the scores sufficiently appropriate for the use you want to make of the scores? How current is the information? When was the instrument developed? How credible are the authors? How long has the instrument been in use? Is there a substantial track record of successful use?

Perhaps the most important characteristic of any assessment is the validity of its results. What validity information has been provided? Do the validity studies provide an indication that the instrument is measuring what it claims to measure? If you are using the instrument to help students increase their occupational possibilities, does the publisher claim that it does this? If so, does the publisher offer studies substantiating that individuals are increasing their occupational options as a result of the information on the instrument? Remember that there is no "valid" test or assessment, but rather there needs to be substantive validity evidence provided by the developer that suggests you can use the results for the purpose you intended.

Are the interpretations made of the results backed up by evidence from the publishers or others?

Read Critiques and Reviews: Before making a final decision on an instrument, it is very helpful to read professionals' critiques of the instrument. These reviews can be found in various books, journals, and newsletters. By all means ask your colleagues and professors about their opinions of the various instruments you are considering.

Be aware that some individuals, although they are rare, may not perform thorough critiques. Some reviews may be written by persons who have not used the instrument or have not even taken it themselves. Some reviewers also do not take into consideration the many improvements made by publishers over the years as new research and information become available, and capabilities change. If you see a review that quotes or comments on information about previous versions of the instrument, you need to be especially careful in determining whether the criticsm is still valid for the current version. Responsible publishers do not hesitate to make changes based on new research and new needs. Be sure the review is up-to-date and based on the version of the instrument you are considering using.

Pay attention to the author of the review and his or her affiliation. Does the reviewer have a stake in the success of that instrument or of a competing product? Sometimes there are philosophical differences between career development professionals; this can come out, sometimes unobtrusively, in a review. It's a good practice to read reviews, but to use that information along with all the other information you have read and collected before making a decision.

Talk With Others Who Use the Instrument: Take advantage of the experience of others who have used the instrument with students or clients similar to those with whom you are working. If you don't know a colleague who is using the instrument, ask the publisher for several customer referrals. Review those names and select a few from the list that are most likely to work in an environment with characteristics similar to yours. Then, by all means, call and talk with the persons who can give you firsthand information. You might discover information that the sales person has not mentioned, the catalog has not described, or that the publisher has not provided in the manuals. Persons who have used the instrument with their students or clients are aware of peculiarities, pitfalls, capabilities, and extraneous information that is not printed in documents or widely disseminated within the career counseling community.

Check the Cost: Does the cost of the inventory match your budget? Some inventories are sold based on a per pupil cost and others are offered by enrollment of your school. Some may be offered free, but there may be a cost for reporting the results. Examine the cost of the instrument compared to the instrument's quality and the information it provides you and the student or client. Also, consider the scoring process; some hand-scored instruments may be less expensive, but it may take more of your time to score and manage.

Sometimes the same instrument is offered via different delivery platforms: paper/pencil, computer, computer network, and/or Internet. Costs may differ as can the kind and amount of information returned to the student and to you.

Instruments offered free may sound inviting initially, but don't be seduced. You need to check to see if there is a catch. There may be no catch at all, as is typical with government sponsored or created instruments that are designed to provide a public service. Other free instruments may not have been developed using proper assessment development procedures; thus, there is no information on reliability and validity. Using assessment without good technical support may actually cause harm to your students or clients by causing them to make decisions based on faulty results.

If an instrument is offered at what seems to be an unusually low cost, ask yourself why. Sometimes Internet-delivered instruments are offered for free or very low cost, but will your students be bombarded with advertising? Will their results be sold to marketers, loan officers, training and educational programs, or other organizations? Check thoroughly before using the instrument. Caveat Emptor!

Take the Assessment Yourself: Taking the assessment yourself is an excellent way to become familiar with an interest inventory, or any assessment for that matter. Contact the publisher and obtain a sample copy of the assessment. Most publishers are willing to provide a copy at no or minimal cost. Even if you have to pay for a copy, it is well worth knowing if the instrument is right for your students or clients before you purchase several copies and find out it is not appropriate or applicable for one reason or another.

By administering the assessment to yourself, you can determine whether the directions are clear and easy to follow, whether the items make sense to you and will to your students or clients, whether the scoring of the instrument is easy, whether the timing is right, and whether the interpretive material is on target with what your student or clients will find informative and helpful. As a final check, you may want to obtain the opinion of a few students or clients to see what they think.

Using a Checklist to Assist Your Decision-Making

You are ultimately responsible for your selection of an interest inventory. It may be helpful to use the checklist on the following page to organize information in a purposeful, systematic, and objective way so that you can easily review each instrument in making a final decision. Look at the information made available by the publisher, read instrument reviews, check with your colleagues, and even share the instrument with your students or clients to gather their opinions in order to make a comfortable decision about which instrument might be best to use. The rest is up to you!

For each instrument you are considering, conduct a review and complete the checklist. Room is provided on the checklist to add some additional criteria that may be particularly pertinent and important to you. If a criterion is not applicable to your situation, leave it blank. When you are done, add up the number of outstanding, acceptable, and not acceptable ratings to see how the instrument matched up to the criteria when compared to other instruments.

Decision-Making Checklist

Instrument Name: _____

Publisher: _____

Evaluation Criteria	Rating		
	Outstanding	Acceptable	Not Acceptable
Assessment's Purpose Matches My Purpose			
Instrument's Target Audience Is Similar to My Students or Clients			
Quality of Technical Information (such as Reliability and Validity) Is Strong			
Development Sample and Norms Represent My Students or Clients			
Delivery Format Is Suitable to My Students or Clients			
Vocabulary Is Appropriate to My Target Audience			
Scoring for My Students or Clients Is Easy, Accurate, and Appropriate			
Scoring Process Minimizes Errors			
Feedback of Results Is Timely and Useful			
Results Reported Are Clear and Helpful			
Recommended Interpretations Are Supported by Research			
Amount and Kind of Interpretation Is Appropriate to the Needs of My Students or Clients (not too much or too little)			
Mechanism for Storing Results Matches My Needs and Organizational Capabilities			
Match Between the Mechanism for Retrieving Results, and My Needs and Organizational Capabilities			
Supportive Documentation Is Available and Provided by the Publisher (such as technical reports and research studies)			
Technical Reviews by Unbiased and Credible Persons Provide Supportive Information			
Information from Colleagues Who Have Used the Instrument Support Its Use			
My Personal Review of the Instrument Supports Its Use			
Students or Clients Who Have Taken the Instrument Support Its Use			
Cost Is in Line with Benefit			
Costs Are Within My Budget			
Add Other Criteria!			
TOTAL			

Chapter 4:

Published Inventories

The previous chapter provided some issues to ponder and criteria you should apply when selecting an interest inventory that is appropriate for your use and that of your students. This chapter provides you some basic information about nine of the most widely used, commercially published, RIASEC-based inventories. This information will give you a start on the analysis you need to do to select the right instrument.

The type of information provided includes basic assessment information such as:

- **Publisher and Author Information** – Contact information for ordering and additional information.

- **Basic Target Audience** – Grade level or age that the publisher has indicated is appropriate for use of their inventories.

- **Versions** – Information on the various versions and formats available fROm the publisher such as paper and pencil, computer, or internet.

- **Costs** – Basic costs of the inventories and scoring.

- **Number of Items** – Number of items that are included in the inventory.

- **Format** – Format in which items are written. For example, activities, occupational titles, or school subjects.

- **Scale** – Indicates whether scales are yes or no, like or dislike, interested or not interested, or unsure.

- **Scoring** – An indication of the kind of scoring services provided and whether the instrument is self-scored.

- **Contents of the Individual User Report** – Information on the kinds of scores that will be provided and how that information is interpreted.

- **Technical Information: Reliability and Validity Summaries** – Overview of the research showing the levels and types of reliability studies that have been done with a brief overview of the validity.

- **Supplementary Information** – A listing of the materials that have been developed to augment the interest inventory such as user's manuals, technical manuals, books, curriculum materials, brochures, etc.

- **Related Research** – Published articles and reviews that give the user additional insight into the technical quality of the inventory.

- **Unique Aspects of the Inventory** – What is special and/or unique about the instrument that would be of interest to potential users.

- **Future Plans** – Changes that can be anticipated in the future.

In reading the descriptions of each of these inventories, you need to be mindful that this information was provided by the publishers themselves. You need to critically review the information to make an initial determination as to which inventory is best for your use.

It is incumbent upon you, before actually deciding on which instrument to use, to dig into the technical characteristics of the inventories and the supplementary material and not just rely upon the information contained in this chapter. Following the suggestions and completing the checklist in Chapter 3 should help you immensely in this important task.

The Inventories represented include:

- Career Assessment Inventory
- Career Decisions Inventory
- The Career Key
- Harrington - O'Shea Career Decision-Making System, Revised
- Interest Profiler
- Kuder Career Search with Person Match
- Self-Directed Search
- Strong Interest Inventory
- UNIACT

Career Assessment Inventory

Name of Instrument: Career Assessment Inventory™ - Enhanced Version and Vocational Version

Author(s): Charles B. Johansson, Ph.D.

Publication Date: Not Reported

Publisher Name: Pearson Assessments

Publisher Address:

Pearson Assessments
5601 Green Valley Drive, 5th Floor
Bloomington, MN 55437

Publisher Phone Number: 800-627-7271

Publisher Web Site: www.PearsonAssessment.com

Applicable Target Audience:

___ elementary
___ middle
✓ secondary
✓ adult

Versions:

✓ paper/pencil
✓ computer
✓ online
✓ Spanish Answer Sheets (Enhanced and Vocational Versions)
✓ other language? French Answer Sheets (Vocational Version for Canada)
___ version for person with disabilities

Costs: See Pearson Assessments Website

CAI™-Enh   http://www.pearsonassessments.com/catalog/pricing/caienhancedprice.pdf

CAI™-Voc   http://www.pearsonassessments.com/catalog/pricing/caivocationalprice.pdf

Number of Items: Enhanced Version ~ 370 items
Vocational Version ~ 305 items

Format:

The Enhanced Version compares an individual's occupational interests to those of individuals in 111 specific careers that reflect a broad range of technical and professional positions in today's workforce. The reading level is 8th grade. This assessment is designed for individuals 15 or older, who may or may not be college-bound.

The Vocational Version compares an individual's vocational interests to those of individuals in 91 specific careers that reflect a range of positions in today's workforce — including skilled trades and technical and service professions — requiring two years or less of post-secondary training. The reading level is 6th grade. This assessment is designed for individuals 15 or older, who plan to enter careers immediately after high school or who plan to attend community college or trade school.

Scale(s):
Five-point rating scale, with responses such as:
- Like Very Much
- Like Somewhat
- Indifferent
- Dislike Somewhat
- Dislike Very Much

Scoring:
- ✓ Internet
- ✓ MICROTEST Q™ Assessment System software
- ✓ Mail-in Scoring Service
- ✓ Optical Scan Scoring

Contents of Individual User Report:

Both Versions: Graphic and narrative test reports can be shared with the client and the narrative report provides a three-page counselor's summary of results. The combined gender scales of the assessment allow for the broadest interpretation of survey results. The inventory uses occupational themes based on the widely accepted RIASEC model to assist in the interpretation and explanation of interest scores.

Profile Report: The profile report provides a graphical depiction of the individual's score on each scale, a list of additional occupations to investigate, and a page of career resources on the web. There is an option to print "Understanding Your Results," an in-depth description of how the results apply to the test taker.

Interpretive Report: The interpretive report presents several pages of graphs and narrative statements that explain the significant score elevations on each scale. It also provides additional reference information relevant to the highest scores, such as a list of additional occupations to investigate and a page of career resources on the web, codes for the page references to the new O*NET codes (SOC-Standard Occupational Classification) and older DOT codes (Dictionary of Occupational Titles) if required, and page references to the Occupational Outlook Handbook. A three-page Counselor's Summary is included, which graphically represents the individual's scores on each scale.

Both versions can be used to help:
- Teach students to focus on the patterns of interest that are important in making educational and occupational choices
- High school and college students identify career directions and major areas of study
- Advise individuals who are re-entering the workforce, considering a career change, or who have been displaced

TECHNICAL INFORMATION

Reliability Information:

Not reported.

Validity Studies:

Not reported.

SUPPLEMENTARY INFORMATION

Supplementary Materials:

Title	Author	Year	Brief Description of Contents	Cost
The O*NET Dictionary of Occupational Titles, 2004 Edition	F. Michael Farr and LaVerne L. Ludden, editors)	2004	This is the only print version of the U.S. Department of Labor's newest data. Containing descriptions of 1,122 jobs, each description includes the O*NET job title and number, the related title from the Occupational Outlook Handbook, job-specific tasks, education and skills needed, average earnings, and cross-references to related occupations.	$39.95

Related Research:

No.	Citation
1.	Kehoe, J.F. (1992). Review of the Career Assesssment Inventory. In J. J. Kramer & J. C. Conoley (eds.), *Eleventh mental measurements yearbook*. Lincoln, NE: Buros Institute, University of Nebraska-Lincoln.

Unique Aspects of Instrument:

Both inventories sample a broad range of occupations. The Enhanced Version more closely matches the distribution of professional and nonprofessional jobs in the labor force and is therefore preferred when assessing groups with a variety of career aspirations.

Future Plans:

Not reported.

Career Decisions Inventory

Name of Instrument: Career Directions Inventory

Author(s): Douglas N. Jackson, Ph.D.

Publication Date: 1986, 2001

Publisher Name: Published simultaneously by Sigma Assessment Systems, Inc. (United States), and Research Psychologists Press, Inc. (Canada)

Publisher Address:

Sigma Assessment Systems, Inc.
511 Fort Street, Suite 435
PO Box 610984
Port Huron, MI 48061-0984
United States

Research Psychologists Press, Inc.
700 Richmond Street, Suite 202
PO Box 3292, Station B
London, ON N6A 4K3
Canada

Publisher Phone Number: 1-800 265-1285

Publisher Web Site: www.sigmaassessmentsystems.com

Applicable Target Audience:

____ elementary
____ middle
✓ secondary
✓ adult

Versions:

✓ paper/pencil
✓ computer (stand-alone)
✓ online
____ Spanish
✓ other language? French
____ version for person with disabilities

Costs:

1) **CDI Examination Kit.** The kit includes the test manual and machine scorable question and answer document for the CDI Extended Report. $25.00

2) **CDI Extended Reports.** Price includes machine scorable question and answer document and computer report.
   - 1 report $13.00
   - 1 to 3 packages (of 10 reports) $90 each package
   - 4 or more packages $80.00 each package

3) **SigmaSoft CDI for Windows**. Includes complete installation package and 10 coupons. $105.00
   SigmaSoft coupons are purchased to generate CDI reports. The CDI Extended Report requires 6 coupons, and the CDI Basic report requires 4 coupons. Coupons are priced as follows:

- 1-99 coupons at $1.90 each
- 100-499 coupons at $1.65 each
- 500 or more coupons at $1.40 each

4) **Online at www.careerinventory.com.** An abbreviated form of the CDI report is available free at this site. The CDI Plus report, which is analogous to the CDI Extended report, is $6.95 for the general public and $4.95 for counselors.

5) **Online at** <u>www.sigmatesting.com</u>**.** Testing professionals and counselors can administer the CDI to clients and/or students for $4.95

Number of Items: 100 triads (300 statements)

Format:

The CDI consists of 100 sets of three statements that describe job-related activities. These statements represent both work roles (for example, Sales and Teaching) and work styles (for example, Assertive, Persuasive, and Systematic). The work styles do not reflect personality traits per se; rather, they reflect preferences for certain work environments. A person could prefer a job where they would need to be persuasive, but not necessarily be capable of being persuasive.

Scale(s):

The CDI items are presented in forced-choice format to reduce the potential for response biases (for example, the tendency to respond "like" to career assessments), which would affect the accuracy of the report. Items are presented in triads and the respondent is asked to select their most and least preferred activity.

Scoring:

   ___ self-scoring
   ✓ CD/machine
   ✓ Internet
   ✓ other Software

Contents of Individual User Report:

The CDI Extended Report contains the following information:

1) A profile of scores on the *15 Basic Interest Scales* followed by a description of the scales. These scores indicate the degree to which respondents will be interested in activities related to the corresponding Basic Interest Scale.
2) A profile of scores on the *7 General Occupational Themes* followed by descriptions of the themes. The results of factor analytic studies indicate that the CDI Basic Interest scales can be represented by 7 broad themes. These themes are similar to Holland's RIASEC codes. The additional theme, Serving, was found consistently in the empirical multivariate studies of the CDI.
3) A profile of scores on the *27 Job Clusters*. Based on multivariate procedures, these clusters were derived from over 100 educational groups. The scores indicate the degree of similarity between the respondent's Basic Interest profile and the pattern of responses of people in the groups defining each cluster.
4) The 'top three' highest ranked Job Clusters are described in more detail. Lists of sample occupations are presented for each cluster with corresponding O*NET codes. O*NET is a website that offers a comprehensive classification of occupational titles and categories based on the Standard Occupation Classification System. Suggested readings, Internet links, and web-based

147

activities, as well as contact information for professional organizations related to each cluster are presented to further career exploration.

5) A profile of scores on *100 Educational Specialty Groups* shows the degree of similarity between the respondent's pattern of interest, and those students in these different educational fields. Such fields include Chemical Engineering Technician, Florist, Social Worker and Advertising Design.

6) Scores on the following four *Administrative Indices* assist in evaluating the dependability of the results: i) Percentage of Scorable Responses, ii) Infrequency Score, iii) Incorrect Items, and iv) Reliability Index. The CDI report also indicates whether these scores are within the normal limits, making it easier to interpret.

7) The last section of the report, *Where to Go From Here*, provides general career related resources (for example, books and suggested activities) for further career exploration.

The *profiles of scores* are presented in terms of percentiles. Listed after each scale, theme, cluster, or group name is the percentile corresponding to the respondent's score computed in terms of both the female and male comparison groups. The plotted profile is based on a comparison with individuals in the comparison group of the same sex as the respondent. The percentiles are based on an updated normative sample of 2500 people (1250 men and 1250 women) developed in 2000.

Basic Interest Scales:
Administration, Art, Clerical, Food Service, Industrial Art, Health Service, Outdoors, Personal Service, Sales, Science, Teaching/Social Service, Writing, Assertive, Persuasive, Systematic.

General Occupational Themes:
Realistic/Practical, Enterprising, Artistic/Communicative, Social/Helping, Investigative/Logical, Conventional, and Serving.

Job Clusters:
Hospitality and Travel Services, Medical and Health Care, Banking and Accounting, Architectural Technology, Drafting and Design, Word Processing and Administrative Assistant, Renewable Resource Technology, Marketing and Merchandising, Skilled Trades, Public and Protective Services, Art, Science and Engineering, Food Services, Agriculture and Animal Science, Social Services, Administration, Electronic Technology, Sales, Health Record Technology, Law Enforcement, Education, Communication Arts, Performing Arts, Administration, Computer and Mathematical Science, Library Science, Personal Care, Funeral Services, and Social Science.

TECHNICAL INFORMATION

Reliability Information:

Test-Retest Reliability. Seventy senior high school students (34 men and 36 women) were given the CDI on two occasions separated by an average of four weeks. The data forming the basis for all of the profiles appearing on the CDI report were correlated for the two occasions and are reported in the CDI Manual. The CDI shows acceptable levels of test-retest reliability for the Basic Interest scales (.72 to .94), General Occupational Themes (.86 to .95), Job Clusters (.76 to .94), and Educational Specialty Groups (.71 to .96).

Internal Consistency Reliability. Internal consistency reliability was appraised using the 1000 respondents drawn from the original normative group. Coefficient alpha was computed for all substantive scales—the Basic Interest scales (.67 to 91), the General Occupational Themes (.86 to .91), Similarity to Job Clusters (.74 to .91), and Similarity to Educational Specialty Groups (.70 to .92). Although coefficient alpha reliabilities are not usually reported for vocational interest measures, they are important sources of information about the psychometric characteristics of scales, particularly if scores are used to place individuals along underlying dimensions and to infer the presence or absence of high and low interests in different areas. In reviewing the above values for test-retest and internal consistency reliability, they appear to be on average quite satisfactory.

Validity Studies:

The validities of the CDI scales were appraised by comparing the distributions of scores on different educational specialty groups and cluster scales obtained by individuals in particular relevant specialty groups with those obtained by the 1000 people forming the normative groups, designated as "people in general." A number of such comparisons have been made in the CDI Manual. For example, on average, people working in Electrical Engineering Technology had higher cumulative percentiles on the Electrical Engineering Technology Scale and Electronic Technology Job Cluster than people in general Engineering Technology. Comparable results were found for the many of the scales versus the people in related occupations.

Overall, there appears to be substantial differentiation between targeted groups and people in general. This differentiation is nearly as strong for the relevant cluster scales as it is for the individual group scales, even though each of the cluster scales was developed using a number of different groups.

SUPPLEMENTARY INFORMATION

Related Research:

No.	Citation
1.	Barak, A., Leong, F. T. L. (Ed), & Barak, A. (Ed). (2001). A cognitive view of the nature of vocational interests: Implications for career assessment, counseling, and research. *Contemporary models in vocational psychology: A volume in honor of Samuel H. Osipow* (pp. 97-131). Mahwah, NJ: Lawrence Erlbaum Associates, Inc., Publishers.
2.	Collier, C. M., Spokane, A. R., & Bazler, J. A. (1998). Appraising science career interests in adolescent girls and boys. *Journal of Career Assessment*, 6(1), 37-48.
3.	Dawes, M. E., Horan, J. J., & Hackett, G. (2000). Experimental evaluation of self-efficacy treatment on technical/scientific career outcomes. *British Journal of Guidance and Counseling*, 28(1), 87-99.
4.	O' Brien, V., Martinez Pons, M., & Kopala, M. (1999). Mathematics self-efficacy, ethnic identity, gender, and career interests related to mathematics and science. *Journal of Educational Research*, 92(4), 231-235.
5.	Panagos, R. J., & DuBois, D. L. (1999). Career self-efficacy development and students with learning disabilities. *Learning Disabilities Research and Practice*, 14(1), 25-34.

Unique Aspects of Instrument:

Psychometrically, the following differentiates the CDI from other career interest measures:
- Advanced methods of item selection and scale construction;
- Up-to-date and continuing compilation of a wide range of specialty groups;
- Use of modern multivariate techniques to identify stable clusters of educational and occupational groupings.

The CareerInventory.Com website allows counselors and administrators to easily set up and administer multiple client accounts with exclusive access to track account activity and review CDI results. This website also provides additional resources, including O*NET job listing classifications and relevant career and education planning information.

Future Plans:

Future plans will entail further development, promotion, and expansion of CareerInventory.com. Recently, the functionality and content of the website has been updated to make it more accessible and convenient for career and guidance counselors.

Career Key

Name of Instrument: The Career Key™

Author(s): Lawrence K. Jones

Publication Date: 1987 initially by Ferguson Publishing Co.

Publisher Name: Currently published by Career Key, Inc.

Publisher Address: 1517 Lincoln Street
Hood River, OR 97301

Publisher Phone Number: N/A

Publisher Web Site: www.careerkey.org

Applicable Target Audience:

- ____ elementary
- ✓ middle
- ✓ secondary
- ✓ adult

Versions:

- ✓ paper/pencil
- ✓ computer (stand-alone)
- ✓ online
- ✓ Spanish
- ✓ other language? Chinese, Romanian
- ____ version for person with disabilities

Costs: Free online; order license to make copies at "eBookStore", 1 copy $4.95, 25 copies $7.95

Number of Items: 66

Format:
Occupations, preferred activities, abilities, self-perceptions, values

Scale(s):
Likert

Scoring:

- ✓ self-scoring *use paper & pencil*
- ____ CD/machine
- ✓ Internet

Contents of Individual User Report:

After completing the Career Key, the instrument is scored and RIASEC codes are provided. Based on the results, potential jobs are given by work groups, level of education required, occupational Information, employment and earnings data from the Occupational Employment Statistics, O*NET codes, occupational characteristics, nature of the job, what tools and equipment are used, how closely workers are supervised, working conditions, typical hours worked, the workplace environment, physical activities and susceptibility to injury, special equipment, and the extent of travel required.

TECHNICAL INFORMATION

Reliability Information:

The self-scorer error rate for a study with 175 college students was 1% for a mistaken high-point code (incorrect first letter of the three-letter summary code) and 4% for a mistaken three-letter code. A study of 265 high school students showed that only 3% made this type of error. One study investigated the internal consistency coefficients for the Career Key scales. They showed a moderate degree of internal consistency, with few exceptions. When the results for men and women were combined, the correlations ranged from .69 to .92, with a mean of .74. Test-retest correlations for a three-week interval ranged from .74 to .88, with a mean of .82.

Validity Studies:

Comparing the Self Directed Search (SDS), and the Career Key (CK) with Holland's Vocational Preference Inventory (VPI), it was found that the SDS and the Career Key both had reasonably close matches (23.3 and 20.4, respectively) with the VPI; there was no significant difference shown between the SDS and CK.

Examining the intercorrelations among the Career Key scales as compared to Holland's hexagonal model showed 44 of the 48 possible relationships were consistent with the theoretical model.

Evidence of criterion-related validity of the Career Key scales was obtained by comparing college students' first letter Career Key code with the first letter code of their major. Forty percent of these comparisons were considered "hits" or matches.

SUPPLEMENTARY INFORMATION

Supplementary Materials: (The publications below are available as digital "epublications." They are purchased and downloaded at the Career Key website.)

Title	Author(s)	Year	Brief Description of Contents	Cost
What Job is Best for You	Lawrence K Jones	2003	This "ebook" assists persons in selecting jobs best for them. It focuses on considering alternatives, examining the consequences of the alternatives, and discovering information about the jobs.	$12.95
Choosing Your College Major	Lawrence K Jones	2003	This "ebook" takes the student step-by-step through the process of selecting a college major.	$12.95
What Color Are Your Feathers?	Lawrence K Jones	2003	This book guides the person to promising careers – those in which the individual is most likely to be satisfied and successful. There are four sections: Summary of Holland's Theory, his 6 personality types, 6 environment types, and how to use Holland's theory to make effective career decisions.	$3.95

The Career Key Manual	Lawrence K Jones	2003	The manual describes the goals, features, and construction of Career Key. Information on the underlying construction is provided. Sections of the manual specify technical aspects of the assessment including reliability, validity, and a summary of 15 years of research.	$14.95
How Parents Can Help Their Children's Career Development	Lawrence K Jones	2003	Describes eight strategies that will have a significant impact on career satisfaction and success. It can be used by parents to work with their sons or daughters.	$3.95
Choosing Classes in High School	Lawrence K Jones & Deana Costner	2003	Lesson plans for a one week, 5-day curriculum that teachers (or other professionals) can use to help students select classes for the next school year. Relates choices to the Career Key results and "Foundation" job skills.	$4.95
The Career Key (English or Spanish)	Lawrence K Jones	2003	The 8-page, paper-pencil version of The Career Key™. A license to make multiple copies can be purchased.	$4.95
Career Key Self Help Modules	Lawrence K Jones	2003	Five of the most popular self-help modules from the website on: decision making, learning about yourself, learning about the world of work, training programs, college majors, and career counseling.	$3.95

Related Research:

No.	Citation
1.	Levinson, E. M., Zeman, H. L., & Ohler, D. L. (2002). A critical evaluation of the web-based version of the Career Key. *Career Development Quarterly, 51*, 26-35.
2.	Jones, L.K. (1990). The Career Key: An investigation of the reliability and validity of its scales and its helpfulness among college students. *Measurement and Evaluation in Counseling and Development, 23*, 67-76.
3.	Jones, L.K., Gorman, S., & Schroeder, C.G. (1989). A comparison between the SDS and the Career Key among career undecided college students. *Career Development Quarterly, 37.* 334-343.
4.	Jones, L. K., Sheffield, D., & Joyner, B. (2000). Comparing the effects of the Career Key with the Self-Directed Search and Job-OE among eighth grade students. *Professional School Counselor, 3*, 238-247.

Unique Aspects of Instrument:

The Career Key is a measure with 15+ years of research evidence in support of its validity and reliability and helpfulness.

The Career Key takes less time to take than similar professional instruments; the Internet version is free and links the occupations identified with extensive occupational information from the Occupational

Outlook Handbook; and more than 25 educational modules help users with career-related issues. 1.8 million people use it annually; approximately 700 schools, colleges, libraries, and agencies link their websites to it.

Future Plans:

Continue to expand its features and offerings. Translate it into other languages and expand its use worldwide.

Harrington - O'Shea Career Decision-Making System, Revised

Name of Instrument: Harrington - O'Shea Career Decision-Making System, Revised

Author(s): Thomas F. Harrington and Arthur J. O'Shea

Publication Date: Manual, 2000; Level 1 and Level 2 materials, 2004

Publisher Name: AGS Publishing

Publisher Address: 4201 Woodland Road
Circle Pines, MN 55014-1796

Publisher Phone Number: 1-800-328-2560

Publisher Web Site: http://www.agsnet.com

Applicable Target Audience:

    ___ elementary
    ✓ middle
    ✓ secondary
    ✓ adult

Versions:

    ✓ paper/pencil
    ✓ computer (stand-alone)
    ✓ online
    ✓ Spanish
    ___ other language?
    ___ version for person with disabilities

Costs: $57.99 for package of 25; $51.99 for 25 or more packages of 25

Number of Items: 120 for Level 2, 96 for Level 1

Format:
The interest survey includes short phrases that the client considers before selecting a response.

Scale(s):
Response choices are Like, Dislike, Can't Make Up Your Mind.

Scoring:
    ✓ self-scoring
    ✓ CD/machine
    ✓ Internet

Contents of Individual User Report:

Describes the types of people in the six interest areas surveyed. Uses the top two interest scales to identify related career clusters. Integrates self-assessed ability, school subject, and work value information to help users better identify career fields that match their interests. Provides education and training required and current employment forecasts for specific occupations to help individuals make informed decisions. Gives occupational information for the jobs where over 95% of the workers in the U.S. are employed.

TECHNICAL INFORMATION

Reliability Information:

Internal Consistency: Level 1 alpha coefficients range from .88 to .93; Students ages 11-20
Level 2 alpha coefficients range from . 92 to .95; Students ages 11-20

Test - Retest: Level 1 done with unemployed adults; .74 to .87, 1- month interval. Several studies with various forms of Level 2 and time lapses have reported retest coefficients ranging from .50 to .94.

Interrater: Since the CDM is self-scored, the authors checked the scorer reliability of the inventory with a sample of lower middle class middle school and high school students. They found 94 percent of the students arrived at the correct code.

Validity Studies:

Construct: Several studies reported data that confirmed that the CDM exhibits the expected correlation patterns of the RIASEC hexagonal model.

Concurrent: 74 concurrent validity studies have demonstrated that many educational and occupational groups have obtained CDM codes very consistent with their *Dictionary of Holland Occupational Codes* and *College Majors Finder* codes.

Predictive: A 12-year follow-up study of 316 college freshmen found that 76 percent had graduated with a major congruent with their freshmen CDM results. A 20-year follow-up found a 58 percent hit rate between high school sophomore results and current occupation.

SUPPLEMENTARY INFORMATION

Supplementary Materials:

Title	Author(s)	Year	Brief Description of Contents	Cost
CDM-Videos: Tour of Your Tomorrow Video Series 2nd ed.	Rich Feller and Joe Vasos	2001	The six-tape series helps students and adults see how the CDM's interest areas relate to job clusters, college majors, and training programs.	$199.99

Related Research:

No.	Citation
1.	O'Shea, A. J., & Harrington, T. F. (2003). Using the Career Decision-Making System – Revised to enhance students' career development. *Professional School Counseling*, 6(4), 280-286.
2.	Campbell, V. L., & Raiff, G. W. (2001). Review of The Harrington-O'Shea Career Decision-Making System Revised (CDM). In J. T. Kapes & E. A. Whittfield (Eds.) A Counselor's Guide to Career Assessment Instruments (4th ed.) (pp. 228-234). Columbus, OH: National Career Development Association.

3.	Freeman, B. (1996). The use and perceived effectiveness of Career Assessment Tools: A survey of high school counselors. *Journal of Career Development, 22*, 185-196.
4.	Harrington, T. F., & Schafer, W. D. (1996). A comparison of self-reported abilities and occupational ability patterns across occupations. *Measurement and Evaluation in Counseling and Development, 28(4)*, 180-190.
5.	Lebo, R. B., Harrington, T. F., & Tilman, R. (1995). Work values similarities among students from six countries. *The Career Development Quarterly, 43(4)*, 350-362.

Unique Aspects of Instrument:

In 1976, the CDM authors developed a self-scoring, self-administered, and self-interpreting career exploration tool based on a model of assessing abilities, interests, values, and occupational information. In the 1980's the CDM integrated the U.S. Department of Labor's Guide for Occupational Exploration, creating a better linkage with interest inventory results and labor market information. In the 1990's the instrument was revised and in 1996 was rated the most effective of 10 career assessment tools evaluated in a national sample of high school counselors. The CDM currently integrates O*NET-based data into its system through its CDMCareerZone online.

Future Plans:

The CDM system's wages and occupational outlook are updated every two years. The Internet version is due for release in the Fall of 2004. It will feature a seamless integration of the CDM and CDMCareerZone, a Department of Labor-based career information system that features user-friendly career briefs, career videos, wages, outlooks, and more.

Interest Profiler

Name of Instrument: O*NET Interest Profiler™

Author(s): Philip M. Lewis, David W. Rivkin

Publication Date: 4/25/2001

Publisher Name: U.S. Department of Labor; c/o National Center for O*NET Development

Publisher Address: 700 Wade Avenue, Daniels Building, 2nd Floor, Room G-222, Raleigh, NC, 27605

Publisher Phone Number: (919) 733-2790

Publisher Website: www.onetcenter.org

Applicable Target Audience:

    ___ Elementary
    ___ Middle
    ✓ secondary
    ✓ adult

Versions:

    ✓ paper/pencil
    ✓ computer (stand-alone)
    ___ Online
    ___ Spanish
    ___ other language?
    ___ version for person with disabilities

Costs: Materials can be downloaded free of charge from www.onetcenter.org. Also, printed sets of materials can be ordered from the Government Printing Office. Prices vary depending on number and types of materials ordered. Ordering information can be found at www.onetcenter.org.

Number of Items: 180

Format:

Work Activities

Scale(s):

Like/dislike

Scoring:

    ✓ self-scoring (Paper/Pencil version)
    ✓ CD/machine (Computerized version)
    ___ Internet

Contents of Individual User Report:

1. Paper and Pencil Version. Users are provided with:
   - Profile of scores. User is instructed to use Primary or Secondary Score to select occupations to explore.
   - Definitions of interest areas. Scores reported in terms of the RIASEC model.

- An activity to identify the level of education, training, and work experience to use when selecting occupations to explore. These levels are referred to as Job Zones.
- Lists of occupations to explore. Lists are sorted by highpoint RIASEC code and Job Zones.
- Information on how their interests relate to the world of work and how they can use that information to help them explore careers.
- Information on the importance of using multiple pieces of information about themselves to explore the world of work and make career decisions.
- Alternative exploration strategies if they are not happy with their interest results.
- Instructions on how to explore occupations in O*NET ONLINE.
- A page to record their interest scores, their primary and secondary interest areas, and occupations they wish to explore.

2. Computerized version. Users are provided with:
   - Profile of scores. Users can print out their interest profile.
   - Definitions of interest areas. Scores are reported in terms of the RIASEC model.
   - An activity to identify the level of education, training, and work experience to use when selecting occupations to explore. These levels are referred to as Job Zones.
   - Lists of occupations to explore. Lists are created based on the user's 6 score interest profile and level of education/training/work experience they wish to pursue.
     -- Users can automatically change their job zone.
     -- Users can choose to search using only one interest code.
     -- Users can print out their list of occupations to explore.
   - Information on how their interests relate to the world of work and how they can use that information to help them explore careers.
   - Information on the importance of using multiple pieces of information about themselves to explore the world of work and make career decisions.
   - Alternative exploration strategies if they are not happy with their interest results.
   - Instructions on how to explore occupations in O*NET ONLINE.

TECHNICAL INFORMATION

Reliability Information:

To examine the reliability of the Interest Profiler (IP), an internal consistency analysis and a stability analysis (i.e., test-retest analysis) was conducted. The primary sample used in the first analysis included over 1200 individuals drawn from four regions across the United States (Michigan; New York; North Carolina; and Utah) and included participants from employment security offices, junior colleges, trade schools, high schools and government sponsored workforce development programs. The sample was diverse in terms of gender, ethnicity, education, and employment status. The sample used for the stability analysis, consisting of approximately 250 individuals, was split between junior college, vocational school, and college students.

The studies indicated that the IP had very high internal consistency estimates ranging from .93 to .96. The stability analysis indicated high correlations between the item responses on two different testing occasions, with test-retest correlations ranging from .79 to .88

Validity Studies:

The developmental samples consisted of over 1700 individuals from across the country (e.g., Florida, Michigan, New York, North Carolina, Texas, and Utah). The sample was diverse in terms of ethnicity, education, and employment status.

159

The convergent, discriminate, and structural validity of the Interest Profiler were examined. Analyses were conducted using results from the Interest Profiler and a similar measure, the Interest Finder (Defense Manpower Data Center, 1995). Analyses focused on the comparability and expected relationships between the scores on each of the instruments, including their factor structure, the patterns of cross-correlations and intercorrelations between the items on each of the RIASEC scales, a classification analysis, and a comparison of the score profiles generated by each instrument.

The structural validity analyses evaluated how well the Holland's RIASEC theory models the relationships among the six scales of the Interest Profiler designed to measure each of the RIASEC constructs. A randomization test of hypothesized order (Rounds, Tracey, & Hubert, 1992) was used to examine the structural validity. In addition, multidimensional scaling was also conducted to examine the circular structure of the data. Overall, the construct validity of the Interest Profiler scales was supported, indicating that Interest Profiler scales measures Holland's RIASEC constructs.

SUPPLEMENTARY INFORMATION

Supplementary Materials:

Title	Author(s)	Year	Brief Description of Contents	Cost
O*NET Interest Profiler Score Report (paper and pencil version)	U.S. Department of Labor, Employment and Training Administration	2000	Users record their interest scores within the score report. The report provides: definitions of the user's interest scores; an exercise to identify the level of education/ training/work experience they wish to pursue; an exercise which enables users to use their primary interest areas and level of education and training to identify O*NET occupations they wish to explore; lists of occupations to explore; and information on how to use O*NET ONLINE to explore occupations.	Free download from www. Onetcenter. org
O*NET Occupations Master List	U.S. Department of Labor, Employment and Training Administration	2000	Expanded lists of O*NET occupations sorted by RIASEC area and level of education and training required. Users can identify occupations to explore using their primary interest area and level of education/ training/work experience they wish to pursue.	Free download from www. Onetcenter. org
O*NET Occupations Combined List: Interests and Work Values	U.S. Department of Labor, Employment and Training Administration	2000	Lists of O*NET occupations sorted by primary interest area, work values area and level of education/training/ work experience required. Users can use their interest results, and results from the O*NET Work Importance Locator to explore O*NET occupations presented in this product.	Free download from www. Onetcenter. org
O*NET Interest Profiler User Guide	U.S. Department of Labor, Employment and Training Administration	2000	This guide provides information to workforce development professionals on the development of the O*NET Interest Profiler and how to effectively use the instrument with clients. Topics presented include administration, scoring and interpretation of results. Challenges that clients might face when taking the instrument are also explored.	Free download from www. Onetcenter. org

160

Related Research:

No.	Citation
1.	Lewis, P., & Rivkin, D. (1999). *Development of the O*NET Interest Profiler.* Raleigh, NC: National Center for O*NET Development.
2.	McCloy, R., Campbell, J., Oswald, F., Lewis, P., and Rivkin, D. (1999). *Linking client assessment profiles to O*NET occupational profiles.* Raleigh, NC: National Center for O*NET Development.
3.	Oswald, F., Campbell, J., McCloy, R., Rivkin, D. & Lewis, P. (1999). *Stratifying occupational units by specific vocational preparation.* Raleigh, NC: National Center for O*NET Development.
4.	Rounds, J., Smith, T., Hubert, L., Lewis, P., & Rivkin, D. (1999). *Development of the occupational interest profiles for O*NET occupations.* Raleigh, NC: National Center for O*NET Development.
5.	Rounds, J., Walker, C.M., Day, S.X., Hubert, L., Lewis, P., & Rivkin, D. (1999). *O*NET Interest Profiler: Reliability, validity, and self-scoring.* Raleigh, NC: National Center for O*NET Development.

Unique Aspects of Instrument:

The O*NET Interest Profiler is based on the most up-to-date knowledge of vocational theory and practice. The instrument is composed of 180 work activities that represent a wide variety of occupations, as well as a broad range of training levels. Designed as a self-assessment tool, many users take, score, and interpret their results with little outside assistance. Users link their results directly to O*NET, the nation's leading source of occupational information. They can also use their results in combination with other O*NET career exploration tools, part of a whole-person assessment approach to career exploration.

Future Plans:

The O*NET Interest Profiler is available free of charge to the public. The instrument has been or is in the process of being incorporated into career exploration programs by both private and public organizations. Programs using the Interest Profiler include Career-One-Stops, employment service centers, career information delivery systems, high schools, vocational schools, community colleges, and colleges.

161

Kuder Career Search with Person Match

Name of Instrument: Kuder® Career Search with Person Match
Author(s): Donald G. Zytowski, Ed.D.
Publication Date: 1999
Publisher Name: National Career Assessment Services, Inc.™
Publisher Address: 210 N. 10th Street
P.O. Box 277
Adel, IA 50003
Publisher Phone Number: 1-800-314-8972
Publisher Web Site: http://www.kuder.com
Applicable Target Audience:

___ elementary
✓ middle
✓ secondary
✓ adult

Versions:

✓ paper/pencil
✓ computer (stand-alone)
✓ online
✓ Spanish
___ other language?
___ version for person with disabilities

Costs: The assessment is available in Self-scored, Mail Back and Internet-based formats. Contact NCASI® for a detailed pricing guide.

Number of Items: 60 triads (180 activities)

Format:
Everyday activities – a verb and an object, such as "take dance lessons"

Scale(s):
Forced choice. Assessment-taker marks activities in each triad as most preferred, next most preferred, and least preferred.

Scoring:

✓ self-scoring
✓ CD/machine
✓ Internet

Contents of Individual User Report:

Interest Profile: Career clusters rank-ordered by interest level illustrated by a bar graph and a percentile score. Aligned to the six Kuder® Career Clusters or may be customized to the Federal 16 Career Clusters or another state specific cluster/pathway system.

Person Match: The top five person matches for each of the top two career clusters (three matches for the top five clusters on Federal clusters report).

Occupation Chart: Sample occupations in each cluster based on education level.

College Grid: Sample college majors in each cluster with two years of post-secondary education or 4+ years.

Additional career planning resources via Internet-based system:
College Search Engine
Links to the Occupational Outlook Handbook and O*NET resources
Access to a personal Kuder® Electronic Career Portfolio
Technical Education Information

TECHNICAL INFORMATION

Reliability Information:

Cluster scores for the online version are generated from scores on the well-known 10 Kuder® Activity Preference scales, which are not reported.

Intercorrelations of the Activity preference Scales range between -.27 and .06, which is typical for forced-choice formatted items.

Median KR-20 is .73 in a range of .64 to .80 (n=146 adults, online administration)
Median temporal reliability is .87 in a range of .83 to .92 (n=73 college students, 2 week interval, online administration)
Median whole profile reliability is .78 (n=90 college students, 3 week interval, pencil and paper administration)

Validity Studies:

Median correlation between Kuder® AP scales and Strong basic scales is .38 for women and .48 for men.
Median correlation between Kuder® AP scales and SDS scales is .45 for women and .50 for men.
Kendall's tau, reflecting rank order concordance between Kuder® cluster scales and their corresponding SII and SDS scales vary between .12 and .56.

SUPPLEMENTARY INFORMATION

Supplementary Materials:

Title	Author(s)	Year	Brief Description of Contents	Cost
Kuder® Career Planning System	Donald G. Zytowski, Ed.D.	2001	Combines the Kuder® Career Search with Person Match interest inventory, the Kuder® Skills Assessment, and Super's work values inventory®—revised with the Kuder® Electronic Portfolio and the Administrative Database Management System. Assessment—takers have access to a variety of online career and college planning resources through the system.	Available for an annual site license based on total building enrollment or on a per unit basis. Call NCASI® for a price quote.

Kuder® Electronic Career Portfolio		2001	Assessment-takers can professionally record their career development activities, educational background, employment experiences, special skills, references, assessment results, etc. The portfolio is the gateway to the online Kuder® Career Planning System and stays with an individual for a lifetime. Users can automatically generate a standard resume with key information entered into the portfolio.	Available free online and included with the online assessment formats.
Develop Your Future™ Career Planning Curriculum	JoAnn Harris-Bowlsbey, Ed.D. and Nancy S. Perry	2001	Career planning curriculum designed to guide middle/jr. high and high school students through the career development process with minimal prep time. The cookbook of lesson plans includes: scripted lesson plans, discussion questions, resource material, experiential activities, student handouts, and a parent guide (with the middle/jr. high school version).	$349.00/manual

Related Research:

No.	Citation
1.	Zytowski, D.G. (2004). Kuder Career Search with Person Match: User manual. http://www.kuder.com/custom/user_manual/
2.	Kuder, F. (1980) Person-matching. *Educational and Psychological Measurement, 40,* 1-8.
3.	Kelly, K.R. (2002). Concurrent validity of the Kuder Career Search activity preference scales and career clusters. *Journal of Career Assessment, 10,* 127-144.

Unique Aspects of Instrument:

The KCS is unique in reporting Person Matches, online links to autobiographical job sketches of a number of individuals whose interest profiles most closely match that of the inventory-taker.

A companion test, the Kuder® Skills Assessment may be taken and compared with interest results in a combined report that suggests actions for various combinations of score levels.

Also featured in the online version are numerous links to educational and occupational information sources, and to the user's personal portfolio, where scores, grades, and other achievements can be stored for use in school and job applications.

Future Plans:

Not Reported.

Self-Directed Search

Name of Instrument: Self-Directed Search® (SDS®)

Author(s): John L. Holland, PhD

Publication Date: SDS Professional User's Guide, 1997
SDS Technical Manual, 1997

Publisher Name: Psychological Assessment Resources, Inc.

Publisher Address: 16204 North Florida Avenue
Lutz, Florida 33549

Publisher Phone Number: 1-800- 331-8378

Publisher Web site: www.parinc.com

Applicable Target Audience:

SDS Form CE: Middle- or junior-high school students
SDS Form CP: Adults
SDS Form E: Adults and older adults with lower educational levels
SDS Form R: High-school students, college students, and adults

Versions:

✓ Paper/pencil (All SDS Forms)
✓ Computer (SDS Forms CE, CP, and R)
✓ Online (SDS Form R: www.self-directed-search.com)
✓ Spanish (SDS Forms E and R only)
✓ Other language? (May be available by special copyright permission, can e-mail custserv@parinc.com if they wish to obtain a specific language version. SDS Forms E and R have English Canadian versions; SDS Form R also has a French Canadian version.)
___ version for person with disabilities

Costs: May change. Current costs are outlined in PAR's catalog and Web site at www.parinc.com. Also, costs depend on the forms used/packages purchased and format (e.g., scoring service, computer version).

Number of Items:

SDS Form CE: 216
SDS Form CP: 216
SDS Form E: 198
SDS Form R: 228

Format:
Occupations and activities ratings for all SDS Forms, as well as self-estimates ratings in ability areas for SDS Forms CE, E, and R.

Scale(s):
Items are like/dislike (SDS Form R) or yes/no (SDS Forms CE, CP, and E).
SDS Forms CE, E, and R have a Self-Estimates section that has a Likert rating from 1-7.

Scoring:

✓ Self-scoring (All SDS Forms)
✓ CD/machine (Software) (SDS Forms CE, CP, R)
✓ Internet (SDS Form R)
✓ Other (PAR Professional Report Service for SDS Forms CP and R)

Contents of Individual User Report:

The personalized reports for SDS Forms CP and R include a description of each of the six RIASEC types; the client's 3-letter Holland code; an explanation of how the code can be used in career planning; a list of occupations and fields of study that match the code; and Next Steps for clients to follow in their career exploration.

The personalized reports for SDS Forms CE and E include a description of each of the six RIASEC types; the client's 2-letter Holland code; an explanation of how the code can be used in career planning; a list of occupations and fields of study that match the code; and Next Steps for clients to follow in their career exploration.

Sample reports for the SDS Form R, CE, and CP are available on PAR's Web site at www.parinc.com/sample_reports.cfm, under the Career Development and Planning subsection.

TECHNICAL INFORMATION

Reliability Information:

For SDS Form R, internal consistency coefficients range from .91 to .93 for high school students, .90 to .93 for college students, and .91 to .94 for adults. Test-retest correlations for intervals from 4 to 12 weeks range from .76 to .89 for a combined sample. Standard Errors of Measurement are below 6 for all scales, with most between 3.00 and 4.00.

Reliability data are similar for the other forms of the SDS. For combined age/gender samples, internal consistency coefficients range from .87 to 93 for Form CP, .94 to .96 for Form E, and .91 to .96 for Form CE.

Validity Studies:

Concurrent validity depends greatly upon the respondent's age, with hits (matches with vocational aspiration or occupation) ranging from 48% for high school students, up to 76% for employed adults. Predictive validity shows a similar range of hits over periods of 1 to 7 years, for a variety of groups from high school through adulthood. These figures demonstrate average to high efficiency when compared with other interest inventories. Scale convergence and independence also support the validity of the SDS, with sections having correlations ranging from .53 to .90 with their summary scales, and from -.10 to .55 with unrelated summary scales.

SUPPLEMENTARY INFORMATION

Supplementary Materials:

See catalog or web site for current pricing.

Title	Author(s)	Year	Brief Description of Contents
Dictionary of Holland Occupational Codes, 3rd edition	Gottfredson, G. D., & Holland, J. L.	1996	Listings of Holland classifications.
The Educational Opportunities Finder™	Rosen, D., Holmberg, K., & Holland, J. L.	1997	Companion instrument to the SDS that enables individuals to identify the fields of study or vocational programs that match their interests, abilities, and personalities.
The Leisure Activities™ Finder	Holmberg, K., Rosen, D., & Holland, J. L.	1997	Companion instrument to the SDS that helps individuals find leisure time activities that match their personality types.
The Self-Directed Search® and Related Holland Career Materials: A Practitioner's Guide	Reardon, R. C., & Lenz, J. G.	1998	Practitioner's guide to understanding the SDS, the SDS Forms, and the RIASEC codes.
Making Vocational Choices, 3rd edition	Holland, J. L.	1997	Practical applications of the RIASEC theory of careers and its successful application to career choice.
You and Your Career	Holland, J. L.	1994	Guide for helping students and clients make career choices.

Related Research:

No.	Citation
1.	Holland, J. (1996). Exploring careers with a typology: What we have learned and some new directions. *American Psychologist, 51*, 397-406.
2.	Holland, J. (1999). Why interest inventories are also personality inventories. In M. Savickas & A. Spokane (Eds.), *Vocational interests: Meaning, measurement, and counseling use* (pp. 87-102). Palo Alto, CA: Davies-Black.
3.	Reardon, R., & Lenz, G. (1999). Holland's theory and career assessment. *Journal of Vocational Behavior, 55*, 102-113.
4.	Savickas, M., & Gottfredson, G. (Eds.) (1999). Holland's theory (1959-1999): Forty years of research and application. *Journal of Vocational Behavior* (special issue), *55*, 1-160.
5.	Spokane, A., & Holland, J. (1995). The Self-Directed Search: A family of self-guided career interventions. *Journal of Career Assessment, 3*, 373-390.

Unique Aspects of Instrument:

Form R: The SDS Form R is an easy-to-use, comprehensive career exploration tool that allows people to gain insight into the world of work and, with their new self-understanding, discover an occupational "match." Individuals answer questions about their aspirations, activities, competencies, occupations, and other self-estimates and discover occupations that best fit their interests and skills.

- Yields a 3-letter Summary Code that designates the three personality types an individual most closely resembles.

- Normative data derived from a nationally representative sample of 2,602 students and working adults.

Other components of the SDS Form R include the Occupations Finder, Alphabetized Occupational Finder, You and Your Career, Leisure Activities Finder, and Educational Opportunities Finder booklets.

Form CE: Designed to introduce the middle- or junior-high school student to educational and vocational exploration, the SDS Form CE is written at a 3rd-grade reading level and is ideally suited for career-oriented classroom activities. Other components of the SDS Form CE are the Careers and Exploring Your Future booklets.

Form E: The SDS Form E asks simple questions about an individual's likes and dislikes, their competencies, the jobs they find interesting, and their personal abilities. Written at a 4th-grade reading level and designed for adults and adolescents at lower educational levels, the SDS Form E focuses on training and jobs that require a high-school diploma or less. Other components include The Jobs Finder and You and Your Job booklets.

Form CP: Designed for adults in career transition and those seeking occupations at upper levels of educational requirements, the SDS Form CP can help individuals affected by organizational changes make successful career transitions; help employees plan for future professional advancement; and help individuals reentering the workforce to establish new career foundations. Other components include The Career Options Finder and Exploring Career Options booklets.

Future Plans:

Not Reported.

Strong Interest Inventory

Name of Instrument: Strong Interest Inventory®
Author(s): E. K. Strong
Publication Date: 1933, 1938, 1945, 1946, 1966, 1968, 1974, 1981, 1985, 1994
Publisher Name: CPP, Inc.
Publisher Address: 3803 East Bayshore Road, Palo Alto, CA 94303
Publisher Phone Number: 1-800-624-1765
Publisher Website: http://www.cpp.com
Applicable Target Audience:

    ____ elementary
    ___ middle
    ✓ secondary
    ✓ adult

Versions:

    ✓ paper/pencil
    ✓ computer (stand-alone)
    ✓ online
    ___ Spanish
    ___ other language?
    ___ version for person with disabilities

Costs: See "Supplementary Information" section

Number of Items: 317

Format:
Occupations, School Subjects, Activities, Leisure Activities, Types of People, Preference Between Two Activities, Your Characteristics, Preference in the World of Work

Scale(s):
Like/Dislike

Scoring:
    ✓ self-scoring
    ✓ CD/machine
    ✓ Internet

Contents of Individual User Report:

See "Supplementary Information" section

TECHNICAL INFORMATION

Reliability Information:

The following information is all taken from the Strong Interest Inventory Applications & Technical Guide (1994).

GOTs: (adults) 3-6 month test-retest reliabilities .84-.92
GOTs: (college students) 1-month test-retest reliabilities .84-.88
GOTs: (college students) 3-month test-retest reliabilities .77-.91
GOTs: (adults) internal consistency Cronbach alphas .90-.94
BISs: (adults) 3-6 month test-retest reliabilities .80-.94
BISs: (college students) 1-month test-retest reliabilities .78-.93
BISs: (college students) 3-month test-retest reliabilities .66-.91
BISs: (adults) internal consistency Cronbach alphas .74-.94
PSSs: (adults) 3-6 month test-retest reliabilities .85-.92
PSSs: (college students) 1-month test-retest reliabilities .83-.91
PSSs: (college students) 3-month test-retest reliabilities .81-.89
PSSs: (adults) internal consistency Cronbach alphas .78-.91
OSs: (adults) 3-6 month test-retest reliabilities .80-.95
OSs: (college students) 1-month test-retest reliabilities .70-.93
OSs: (college students) 3-month test-retest reliabilities .69-.94

Validity Studies:

General Occupational Themes and the Basic Interest Scales: The General Reference Sample consists of 9,467 women and 9,484 men. The General Reference Sample is composed of samples of approximately 200 members of each occupational group.

Criterion Related Validity: The validity of each of the Basic Interest Scales can be evaluated by ranking the means of the 109 occupational groups in the 1994 Strong on each scale. The results suggest substantial validity for the Basic Interest Scales.

Construct Validity: Extensive construct validity information is provided in the *Strong Interest Applications and Technical Guide.*

SUPPLEMENTARY INFORMATION

Supplementary Materials:

Title	Author(s)	Year	Brief Description of Contents	Cost
Strong Profile		1994	Provides overview of GOT, BIS, OS, and PSS results.	$7.80
Strong High School Profile	Sandra Rumpel and Kathleen D. Lecertua	1996	Provides overview of GOT, BIS, OS, and PSS results. Includes post-secondary options, ideas for work-study and summer jobs, and identifies career and educational options.	$7.80
Strong College Profile	Jeffrey P. Prince	2001	Provides overview of GOT, BIS, OS, and PSS results. Explores academic majors, campus activities, and identifies career and educational options.	$7.80
Strong Interpretive Report	Allen L. Hammer and Judith Grutter	1994	Provides practical applications and suggestions to begin the career development process.	$14.20
Strong Professional Report	Allen L. Hammer	1994	Identifies professional occupations that typically require a four-year college education.	$17.00

Career Enrichment Report	Allen L. Hammer and David Donnay	2001	Helps employees find their organizational fit by applying information from the Strong instrument to the organizational setting.	$13.80
Career Transition Report	Allen L. Hammer and David Donnay	2001	Assists outplaced employees and others undergoing career transition or workforce reentry in exploring options and planning new career directions.	$13.80
Strong & MBTI® Career Report	Judith Grutter and Allen L. Hammer	1994	Provides career information using a combination of Strong and MBTI® results.	$13.45
Strong & MBTI® Entrepreneur Report	Allen L. Hammer	1994	Combines information from the Strong and MBTI® instruments to provide an in-depth look at entrepreneurial potential.	$13.45
Strong Interest Explorer	Judy Chartrand	2001	Self-scorable booklet contains condensed number of items. Ideal for students and individuals exploring new career directions or reentering the workforce.	$45.00 (pkg 10)
Strong Applications and Technical Guide	Lenore W. Harmon, Jo-Ida C. Hansen, Fred H. Borgen, and Allen L. Hammer	1994	Provides valuable information to assist in the administration and interpretation of the Strong instrument.	$75.00
Where Do I Go Next?	Fred Borgen and Judith Grutter	1995	Interpretive booklet that enables clients to better understand career interests by providing expanded information on GOT, BIS, and PSS.	$6.00
Career Exploration: A Journey of Discovery	Allen L. Hammer	1994	Interactive worksheet that guides client's self-assessment by integrating abilities, values, interests, and goals.	$22.50 (pkg 25)

Related Research:

No.	Citation
1.	Harmon, L. W., Hansen, J. C., Borgen, F. H., & Hammer, A. L. (1994). *Strong Interest Inventory Applications and Technical Guide.* Stanford, CA: Stanford University Press.
2.	Donnay, D.A.C. (1997). *E.K. Strong's Legacy and Beyond: 70 Years of the Strong Interest Inventory.* Career Development Quarterly, *46*, 2-22.
3.	Hansen, J. C. (2000). Interpretation of the Strong Interest Inventory. In S. H. Osipow (Ed.), *Testing and Assessment in Counseling Practice* (pp. 227-262). Mahwah, NJ: Lawrence Erlbaum Associates, Inc.
4.	Prince, J. P., & Heiser, L. J. (2000). *Essentials of Career Interest Assessment.* New York: John Wiley & Sons, Inc.
5.	Lattimore, R. R., & Borgen, F. H. (1999). Validity of the Strong Interest Inventory with racial and ethnic groups in the United States. *Journal of Counseling Psychology, 46*, 185-195.

Unique Aspects of Instrument:

The Strong measures clients' interests in a broad range of occupations, work activities, leisure activities, and school subjects. Its validity and reliability far exceed those of any other interest inventory:

- Sample base represents a wide range of educational, ethnic, and socioeconomic levels
- Instrument includes results on the 6 Holland Themes, 25 basic interests, 109 contemporary occupations, and 4 personal styles

Future Plans:

Revision of Strong Interest Inventory® instrument and product line – phase 1 to be released in 2005.

UNIACT

Name of Instrument: UNIACT (Unisex Edition of the ACT Interest Inventory)
Author(s):   ACT, Inc.
Publication Date: 1995
Publisher Name: ACT, Inc.
Publisher Address:

> ACT, Inc.
> 500 ACT Drive
> P.O. Box 168
> Iowa City, IA 52243-0168

Publisher Phone Number: 319-337-1000
Publisher Website: www.act.org
Applicable Target Audience:

- ___ elementary
- ✓ middle
- ✓ secondary
- ✓ adult

Versions:

- ✓ paper/pencil (ACT Assessment, PLAN, EXPLORE, Career Planning Survey)
- ✓ computer (DISCOVER—Windows version)
- ✓ online (DISCOVER—Internet version and Middle School version)
- ___ Spanish
- ___ other language?
- ___ version for person with disabilities

Costs: Vary by program.

Number of Items: 90 (15 items per scale)

Format:
UNIACT is intended for persons in the early stages of career exploration. Items emphasize work-relevant activities that are familiar to people, either through participation or observation. Occupational titles and job duties are not used, because persons in the early stages of career exploration may be unfamiliar with them.

Scale(s):
UNIACT uses a three-choice response format: Dislike, Indifferent, Like.

Scoring:

- ___ self-scoring
- ✓ CD/machine
- ✓ Internet

Contents of Individual User Report:

UNIACT is a component of five ACT programs: DISCOVER, the Career Planning Survey, the ACT Assessment, PLAN, and EXPLORE. Score report content varies by program. DISCOVER and the Career

Planning Survey provide score profiles. All five programs provide occupational options via ACT's unique interpretive aid, the World-of-Work Map. The World-of-Work Map is an extension of Holland's six types, displaying 26 Career Areas (groups of similar occupations) according to their involvement with the basic work tasks that underlie Holland's types. The Map is an empirically based bridge connecting interest scores and relevant occupational options. Users see the "big picture" differences among Career Areas, while being encouraged to focus in on occupations consistent with their UNIACT results. Information and resources are provided for over 550 occupations.

TECHNICAL INFORMATION

Reliability Information:

Internal consistency reliability estimates were obtained for three national samples. Reliabilities ranged from .85 to .91 for grade 8, from .87 to .92 for grade 10, and from .86 to .93 for grade 12.

Test-retest stability coefficients were obtained for a sample of 11th graders who completed UNIACT once and again 1 to 8 months later (average 5 months). Coefficients ranged from .68 to .78 for males (median of .75), and from .69 to .82 (median of .78) for females.

These are examples. More reliability information for a range of age groups are discussed in the *UNIACT Technical Manual*.

Validity Studies:

If a group classified into one of Holland's six types obtains a high-point code via measured interests that matches their type, this is evidence of criterion validity. Over the past 30 years, ACT has collected data from 616 groups, representing over 78,000 persons across age groups. The rate of correct matches is 73%, far exceeding the chance rate (17%).

If scales exhibit the relationships posited by Holland's theory, this is evidence of construct validity. These relationships have been consistently found for UNIACT scales across diverse age groups and racial/ethnic groups.

SUPPLEMENTARY INFORMATION

Supplementary Materials:

Title	Author	Year	Brief Description of Contents	Cost
UNIACT Technical Manual	ACT	1995	Chapters covering characteristics, rationale, development, norms, reliability, and four chapters on validity.	Single copies available free of charge upon request.
DISCOVER Support Materials (Toolkit and Professional Manual)	ACT	On Web	Toolkit contains materials for offline use to assist counselors helping clients with career planning needs. Professional Manual describes uses of DISCOVER, as well as content and theory of assessment components.	Provided with subscription. Also available to non-subscribers free of charge upon request.

Research Support for DISCOVER Assessment Components	ACT	2001	Provides a brief overview of content and validity of DISCOVER assessment components, as well as an overview of the World-of-Work Map.	Single copies available free of charge upon request.
Career Planning Survey Counselor's Manual and Technical Manual	ACT	2001 (both manuals)	Counselor's Manual provides an overview of assessment components, as well as guidelines for score report interpretation. Technical Manual documents psychometric information, with emphasis on the Inventory of Work-Relevant Abilities.	Single copies available free of charge upon request.

Related Research:

No.	Citation
1.	Prediger, D., & Swaney, K. (1995). Using UNIACT in a comprehensive approach to assessment for career planning. *Journal of Career Assessment, 3*, 429-451.
2.	Prediger, D. (2002). Abilities, Interests, and Values: Their assessment and their integration via the World-of-Work Map. *Journal of Career Assessment, 10*, 209-232.
3.	Day, S., Rounds, J., & Swaney, K. (1998). The structure of vocational interests for diverse racial/ethnic groups. *Psychological Science, 9*, 40-44.
4.	Prediger, D., & Vansickle, T. (1992). Locating occupations on Holland's hexagon: Beyond RIASEC. *Journal of Vocational Behavior, 40*, 111-128.

Unique Aspects of Instrument:

- Takes only a few minutes to complete.
- One of the most administered psychological assessments in the world—UNIACT is completed by over 4 million persons each year.
- Extensive research base and ongoing development by ACT staff.
- Published research documents validity for African Americans, Asian Americans, Mexican Americans, and Native Americans.
- Results for all Holland-type assessments are expressed via the World-of-Work Map, helping users compare results across domains and understand their results as a whole.
- UNIACT items have been carefully written to assess basic interests while minimizing the effects of sex-role connotations.

Future Plans:

Over the next few years a shorter version of UNIACT will be introduced in selected ACT programs. Research indicates that this shorter version will retain the validity for career counseling purposes of the current, longer version.

Appendix A:

Occupations by RIASEC
Interest Area and Job Zone

The information in Appendix A was developed by the U.S. Department of Labor, Employment and Training Administration. It is part of their Score Report for the Interest Profiler.

The occupations are listed by the interest areas of Realistic, Investigative, Artistic, Social, Enterprising, and Conventional. They are further organized by what the Department of Labor calls Job Zones. Job Zones are five categories that represent the amount of preparation generally required by the occupation. Included in the concept of preparation is the overall experience needed, the amount of education required, and the amount of job training generally needed. Job Zone 1 requires the least amount of preparation, and Job Zone 5 requires the greatest preparation.

Job Zone 1: Little or No Preparation Needed. People in these occupations generally need no previous work experience or specialized skills. They may require a GED or high school diploma. Some of the occupations may need specialized training, but most often the training needed is on-the-job and from a few days to a few weeks in length.

Job Zone 2: Some Preparation Needed. People in these occupations may find it helpful to have some work experience along with a high school diploma and specialized vocational or job-related training. For some of the occupations, an associate's degree or even a bachelor's degree may be needed. People entering these occupations will probably need a few weeks to a few months of on-the-job experience.

Job Zone 3: Medium Preparation Needed. For these occupations, people generally require some previous work-related experience, skill, and knowledge. Some of the occupations may require an apprenticeship. Although a bachelor's degree may be required, most of the occupations will need training in vocational programs, or an associate's degree. The amount of training is generally one to two years in formal programs and/or on-the-job.

Job Zone 4: Considerable Preparation Needed. Most occupations in this category require at least two to four years of experience, knowledge, and work-related skills. Most require a bachelor's degree.

Job Zone 5: Extensive Preparation Needed. Many years of experience are needed for these occupations. Generally a bachelor's degree is the minimum and some occupations may require a master's, doctor's, or professional degree. As with nearly all occupations, some on-the-job training is needed, but people who enter these occupations are assumed to have the required skills, knowledge, and experience.

Note the numbers preceding each occupational title. They are called ONET/SOC Codes. These are useful for persons who wish to research the details of the occupation on http://www.online.onetcenter.org. The ONET/SOC number is entered and the information for that occupations is provided on the web site.

REALISTIC OCCUPATIONS

REALISTIC — JOB ZONE 1 (Little or No Preparation Needed)

39-3091.00 Amusement and Recreation Attendants
51-3093.00 Food Cooking Machine Operators and Tenders
35-2021.00 Food Preparation Workers
45-4011.00 Forest and Conservation Workers
53-7062.03 Freight, Stock, and Material Movers, Hand
45-2092.02 General Farmworkers
47-3011.00 Helpers—Brick masons, Block masons, Stonemasons, and Tile and Marble Setters
49-9098.00 Helpers—Installation, Maintenance, and Repair Workers
37-3011.00 Landscaping and Grounds keeping Workers
51-6011.03 Laundry and Dry cleaning Machine Operators and Tenders, Except Pressing
51-9123.00 Painting, Coating, and Decorating Workers
53-6021.00 Parking Lot Attendants
51-5023.09 Printing Press Machine Operators and Tenders
51-9061.05 Production Inspectors, Testers, Graders, Sorters, Samplers, Weighers
51-9198.01 Production Laborers
51-9141.00 Semiconductor Processors
51-6031.01 Sewing Machine Operators, Garment
43-5081.01 Stock Clerks, Sales Floor
53-3033.00 Truck Drivers, Light or Delivery Services
51-4121.01 Welders, Production

REALISTIC — JOB ZONE 2 (Some Preparation Needed)

45-2091.00 Agricultural Equipment Operators
49-3023.02 Automotive Specialty Technicians
19-4021.00 Biological Technicians
47-2061.00 Construction Laborers
35-2011.00 Cooks, Fast Food
53-7032.01 Excavating and Loading Machine Operators
47-2073.01 Grader, Bulldozer, and Scraper Operators
47-3013.00 Helpers—Electricians
29-2012.00 Medical and Clinical Laboratory Technicians
31-9093.00 Medical Equipment Preparers
39-3021.00 Motion Picture Projectionists
33-2011.01 Municipal Fire Fighters
51-4011.01 Numerical Control Machine Tool Operators and Tenders, Metal and Plastic
37-2021.00 Pest Control Workers
51-9132.00 Photographic Processing Machine Operators
51-4072.01 Plastic Molding and Casting Machine Setters and Set- Up Operators
51-6041.00 Shoe and Leather Workers and Repairers
53-3032.02 Tractor-Trailer Truck Drivers
51-8031.00 Water and Liquid Waste Treatment Plant and System Operators
51-4121.02 Welders and Cutters

REALISTIC — JOB ZONE 3 (Medium Preparation Needed)

49-3023.01 Automotive Master Mechanics
51-3011.01 Bakers, Bread and Pastry
39-5011.00 Barbers

19-4031.00 Chemical Technicians
17-3011.02 Civil Drafters
35-2014.00 Cooks, Restaurant
51-9081.00 Dental Laboratory Technicians
49-2094.00 Electrical and Electronics Repairers, Commercial and Industrial Equipment
47-2111.00 Electricians
11-9012.00 Farmers and Ranchers
45-1011.03 First-Line Supervisors and Manager/Supervisors - Animal Care Workers, Except Livestock
37-1012.02 First-Line Supervisors and Manager/Supervisors - Landscaping Workers
33-3031.00 Fish and Game Wardens
51-9061.01 Materials Inspectors
27-4013.00 Radio Operators
47-2221.00 Structural Iron and Steel Workers
29-2055.00 Surgical Technologists
53-7121.00 Tank Car, Truck, and Ship Loaders
51-6093.00 Upholsterers
31-9096.00 Veterinary Assistants and Laboratory Animal Caretakers

** The occupation was assigned to the group based on its second highest interest area.
*** The occupation was assigned to the group based on its third highest interest area.

REALISTIC — JOB ZONE 4 (Considerable Preparation Needed)

45-2011.00 Agricultural Inspectors
53-2011.00 Airline Pilots, Copilots, and Flight Engineers
17-3011.01 Architectural Drafters
47-2031.01 Construction Carpenters
49-2011.02 Data Processing Equipment Repairers
43-9031.00 Desktop Publishers
49-9051.00 Electrical Power-Line Installers and Repairers
17-3023.01 Electronics Engineering Technicians
39-4011.00 Embalmers
19-1032.00 Foresters
51-9071.01 Jewelers
51-4041.00 Machinists
51-2041.01 Metal Fabricators, Structural Metal Products
33-1021.01 Municipal Fire Fighting and Prevention Supervisors
47-2141.00 Painters, Construction and Maintenance
51-9195.02 Precision Pattern and Die Casters, Nonferrous Metals
13-1041.05 Pressure Vessel Inspectors
29-2034.02 Radiologic Technicians
27-2012.05 Technical Directors/Managers
51-4121.03 Welder-Fitters

REALISTIC — JOB ZONE 5 (Extensive Preparation Needed)

17-2021.00 Agricultural Engineers**
19-1011.00 Animal Scientists**
17-2041.00 Chemical Engineers**
51-5022.08 Dot Etchers
49-2095.00 Electrical and Electronics Repairers, Powerhouse, Substation, and Relay

179

17-2071.00 Electrical Engineers**
51-5022.10 Electrotypers and Stereotypers
33-1021.02 Forest Fire Fighting and Prevention Supervisors
19-2042.01 Geologists**
51-5021.00 Job Printers
17-2121.02 Marine Architects
17-2121.01 Marine Engineers
17-2131.00 Materials Engineers**
19-1022.00 Microbiologists**
51-5023.02 Offset Lithographic Press Setters and Set-Up Operators

17-2171.00 Petroleum Engineers
53-5021.03 Pilots, Ship
51-5022.11 Plate Finishers
27-1013.04 Sculptors**
53-5031.00 Ship Engineers

** The occupation was assigned to the group based on its second highest interest area.
*** The occupation was assigned to the group based on its third highest interest area.

INVESTIGATIVE OCCUPATIONS

INVESTIGATIVE — JOB ZONE 1 (Little or No Preparation Needed)

45-2093.00 Farmworkers, Farm and Ranch Animals***
45-4011.00 Forest and Conservation Workers**
INVESTIGATIVE — JOB ZONE 2 (Some Preparation Needed)
19-4011.01 Agricultural Technicians**
19-4021.00 Biological Technicians**
29-2041.00 Emergency Medical Technicians and Paramedics***
19-4011.02 Food Science Technicians**
33-2022.00 Forest Fire Inspectors and Prevention Specialists***
29-2012.00 Medical and Clinical Laboratory Technicians**
51-9082.00 Medical Appliance Technicians**

INVESTIGATIVE — JOB ZONE 3 (Medium Preparation Needed)

45-2021.00 Animal Breeders**
29-2031.00 Cardiovascular Technologists and Technicians
19-4031.00 Chemical Technicians**
19-4061.01 City Planning Aides**
13-1072.00 Compensation, Benefits, and Job Analysis Specialists
15-1051.00 Computer Systems Analysts
51-9081.00 Dental Laboratory Technicians**
49-2094.00 Electrical and Electronics Repairers, Commercial and Industrial Equipment**
47-2111.00 Electricians**
13-1041.01 Environmental Compliance Inspectors
19-4091.00 Environmental Science and Protection Technicians, Including Health
33-3031.00 Fish and Game Wardens**
17-3026.00 Industrial Engineering Technicians
13-1031.02 Insurance Adjusters, Examiners, and Investigators**
49-9062.00 Medical Equipment Repairers**
19-4051.02 Nuclear Monitoring Technicians**
29-2091.00 Orthotists and Prosthetists**
29-1126.00 Respiratory Therapists
19-3041.00 Sociologists
31-9096.00 Veterinary Assistants and Laboratory Animal Caretakers**

** The occupation was assigned to the group based on its second highest interest area.
*** The occupation was assigned to the group based on its third highest interest area.

INVESTIGATIVE — JOB ZONE 5 (Extensive Preparation Needed)

17-2021.00 Agricultural Engineers
25-1041.00 Agricultural Sciences Teachers, Postsecondary
19-1011.00 Animal Scientists
25-4011.00 Archivists
19-1020.01 Biologists
25-1021.00 Computer Science Teachers, Postsecondary
29-1021.00 Dentists, General
19-3011.00 Economists
17-2071.00 Electrical Engineers
19-2041.00 Environmental Scientists and Specialists, Including Health
29-1062.00 Family and General Practitioners
13-2051.00 Financial Analysts
19-2042.01 Geologists
15-2021.00 Mathematicians
11-9121.00 Natural Sciences Managers
19-2012.00 Physicists
17-2111.03 Product Safety Engineers
29-1066.00 Psychiatrists
29-1067.00 Surgeons
29-1131.00 Veterinarians

INVESTIGATIVE — JOB ZONE 4 (Considerable Preparation Needed)

19-3091.02 Archeologists
17-2061.00 Computer Hardware Engineers
15-1021.00 Computer Programmers
15-1032.00 Computer Software Engineers, Systems Software
13-1041.06 Coroners
15-1061.00 Database Administrators
29-1031.00 Dietitians and Nutritionists
33-2021.02 Fire Investigators
19-1012.00 Food Scientists and Technologists
19-4092.00 Forensic Science Technicians
17-2111.01 Industrial Safety and Health Engineers
19-3021.00 Market Research Analysts
15-3011.00 Mathematical Technicians
19-1042.00 Medical Scientists, Except Epidemiologists
29-1051.00 Pharmacists
29-1071.00 Physician Assistants

19-1031.01 Soil Conservationists
15-2041.00 Statisticians
17-1022.00 Surveyors
19-3051.00 Urban and Regional Planners

** The occupation was assigned to the group based on its second highest interest area.
*** The occupation was assigned to the group based on its third highest interest area.

ARTISTIC OCCUPATIONS

ARTISTIC — JOB ZONE 1 (Little or No Preparation Needed)

39-9011.00 Child Care Workers**
51-9194.05 Etchers, Hand**
41-9012.00 Models

ARTISTIC — JOB ZONE 2 (Some Preparation Needed)

39-6031.00 Flight Attendants***
27-1023.00 Floral Designers
39-5091.00 Makeup Artists, Theatrical and Performance
51-9131.03 Photographic Hand Developers**
27-3011.00 Radio and Television Announcers
27-2042.01 Singers
51-6041.00 Shoe and Leather Workers and Repairers**
39-6022.00 Travel Guides***
37-3013.00 Tree Trimmers and Pruners**

ARTISTIC — JOB ZONE 3 (Medium Preparation Needed)

27-2011.00 Actors
27-3043.03 Caption Writers
51-9194.02 Engraver/Carvers**
51-9194.03 Etchers**
27-1022.00 Fashion Designers
27-3091.00 Interpreters and Translators
49-9063.01 Keyboard Instrument Repairers and Tuners**
27-1026.00 Merchandise Displayers and Window Trimmers
25-4013.00 Museum Technicians and Conservators
49-9063.04 Percussion Instrument Repairers and Tuners**
27-4021.02 Photographers, Scientific
51-9131.01 Photographic Retouchers and Restorers
27-4021.01 Professional Photographers
39-9032.00 Recreation Workers**
27-1013.02 Sketch Artists
19-3041.00 Sociologists**
27-4014.00 Sound Engineering Technicians**
51-9195.03 Stone Cutters and Carvers**
49-9063.02 Stringed Instrument Repairers and Tuners**
27-2012.04 Talent Directors

** The occupation was assigned to the group based on its second highest interest area.
*** The occupation was assigned to the group based on its third highest interest area.

ARTISTIC — JOB ZONE 4 (Considerable Preparation Needed)

11-2011.00 Advertising and Promotions Managers
17-1011.00 Architects, Except Landscape and Naval
27-1011.00 Art Directors

27-3021.00 Broadcast News Analysts
27-4031.00 Camera Operators, Television, Video, and Motion Picture
27-1013.03 Cartoonists
27-1021.00 Commercial and Industrial Designers
39-3092.00 Costume Attendants
27-3043.02 Creative Writers
25-4012.00 Curators
27-2031.00 Dancers
27-3041.00 Editors
27-1027.02 Exhibit Designers
27-1024.00 Graphic Designers
27-1025.00 Interior Designers
25-4021.00 Librarians
27-1013.01 Painters and Illustrators
27-3043.01 Poets and Lyricists
27-2012.01 Producers
27-3022.00 Reporters and Correspondents

** The occupation was assigned to the group based on its second highest interest area.
*** The occupation was assigned to the group based on its third highest interest area.

ARTISTIC — JOB ZONE 5 (Extensive Preparation Needed)

25-1121.00 Art, Drama, and Music Teachers, Postsecondary
27-2032.00 Choreographers
21-2011.00 Clergy**
27-2041.03 Composers
19-3031.03 Counseling Psychologists***
21-2021.00 Directors, Religious Activities and Education***
25-1063.00 Economics Teachers, Postsecondary***
25-1123.00 English Language and Literature Teachers, Postsecondary
25-1124.00 Foreign Language and Literature Teachers, Postsecondary
25-1125.00 History Teachers, Postsecondary***
17-1012.00 Landscape Architects
27-2041.01 Music Directors
27-2042.02 Musicians, Instrumental
19-3094.00 Political Scientists**
29-1066.00 Psychiatrists**
25-1066.00 Psychology Teachers, Postsecondary***
27-1013.04 Sculptors
27-1027.01 Set Designers
25-1067.00 Sociology Teachers, Postsecondary***
27-3042.00 Technical Writers

SOCIAL OCCUPATIONS

SOCIAL — JOB ZONE 1 (Little or No Preparation Needed)

53-3011.00 Ambulance Drivers and Attendants, Except Emergency Medical Technicians
33-3011.00 Bailiffs
35-3011.00 Bartenders**
53-3021.00 Bus Drivers, Transit and Intercity**
39-9011.00 Child Care Workers
35-3022.00 Counter Attendants, Cafeteria, Food Concession, and Coffee Shop
33-9091.00 Crossing Guards
41-9011.00 Demonstrators and Product Promoters**
35-3041.00 Food Servers, Non restaurant
39-4021.00 Funeral Attendants
31-1011.00 Home Health Aides
43-4111.00 Interviewers, Except Eligibility and Loan**
39-3093.00 Locker Room, Coat room, and Dressing Room Attendants
39-5092.00 Manicurists and Pedicurists**
43-4171.00 Receptionists and Information Clerks***
33-9032.00 Security Guards
39-6021.00 Tour Guides and Escorts
39-6032.00 Transportation Attendants, Except Flight Attendants and Baggage Porters**
39-3031.00 Ushers, Lobby Attendants, and Ticket Takers
35-3031.00 Waiters and Waitresses

SOCIAL — JOB ZONE 2 (Some Preparation Needed)

33-9011.00 Animal Control Workers
43-4061.01 Claims Takers, Unemployment Benefits**
29-2041.00 Emergency Medical Technicians and Paramedics
39-6031.00 Flight Attendants**
33-9092.00 Lifeguards, Ski Patrol, and Other Recreational Protective Service Workers**
31-1012.00 Nursing Aides, Orderlies, and Attendants
31-2012.00 Occupational Therapist Aides
31-2011.00 Occupational Therapist Assistants
39-9021.00 Personal and Home Care Aides
31-2022.00 Physical Therapist Aides
31-2021.00 Physical Therapist Assistants
43-5031.00 Police, Fire, and Ambulance Dispatchers
33-9021.00 Private Detectives and Investigators**
31-1013.00 Psychiatric Aides
27-3011.00 Radio and Television Announcers**
41-9022.00 Real Estate Sales Agents**
33-3051.03 Sheriffs and Deputy Sheriffs
21-1093.00 Social and Human Service Assistants
41-3041.00 Travel Agents**
43-4061.02 Welfare Eligibility Workers and Interviewers

SOCIAL — JOB ZONE 3 (Medium Preparation Needed)

39-2011.00 Animal Trainers
31-9091.00 Dental Assistants
29-2021.00 Dental Hygienists
13-1071.01 Employment Interviewers, Private or Public Employment Service
39-9031.00 Fitness Trainers and Aerobics Instructors

35-9031.00 Hosts and Hostesses, Restaurant, Lounge, and Coffee Shop**
27-3091.00 Interpreters and Translators**
41-3021.00 Insurance Sales Agents**
29-2061.00 Licensed Practical and Licensed Vocational Nurses
31-9092.00 Medical Assistants
29-2091.00 Orthotists and Prosthetists
13-2052.00 Personal Financial Advisors
13-1071.02 Personnel Recruiters**
33-3051.01 Police Patrol Officers
21-1092.00 Probation Officers and Correctional Treatment Specialists
29-2053.00 Psychiatric Technicians
27-3012.00 Public Address System and Other Announcers
39-9032.00 Recreation Workers
39-9041.00 Residential Advisors
25-9041.00 Teacher Assistants

** The occupation was assigned to the group based on its second highest interest area.
*** The occupation was assigned to the group based on its third highest interest area.

SOCIAL — JOB ZONE 4 (Considerable Preparation Needed)

29-2051.00 Dietetic Technicians
11-9032.00 Education Administrators, Elementary and Secondary School
21-1012.00 Educational, Vocational, and School Counselors
25-2021.00 Elementary School Teachers, Except Special Education
21-1022.00 Medical and Public Health Social Workers
21-1023.00 Mental Health and Substance Abuse Social Workers
25-2022.00 Middle School Teachers, Except Special and Vocational Education
19-1031.03 Park Naturalists
29-1123.00 Physical Therapists
29-1125.00 Recreational Therapists
29-1111.00 Registered Nurses
25-2031.00 Secondary School Teachers, Except Special and Vocational Education
25-3021.00 Self-Enrichment Education Teachers
11-9151.00 Social and Community Service Managers
25-2042.00 Special Education Teachers, Middle School
25-2041.00 Special Education Teachers, Preschool, Kindergarten, and Elementary School
25-2043.00 Special Education Teachers, Secondary School
29-1127.00 Speech-Language Pathologists
13-1073.00 Training and Development Specialists
25-2032.00 Vocational Education Teachers, Secondary School

SOCIAL — JOB ZONE 5 (Extensive Preparation Needed)

25-1061.00 Anthropology and Archeology Teachers, Postsecondary
23-1022.00 Arbitrators, Mediators, and Conciliators**
25-1062.00 Area, Ethnic, and Cultural Studies Teachers, Postsecondary
29-9091.00 Athletic Trainers
21-2011.00 Clergy

182

19-3031.03 Counseling Psychologists
21-2021.00 Directors, Religious Activities and Education
25-1063.00 Economics Teachers, Postsecondary
25-1123.00 English Language and Literature Teachers, Postsecondary**
25-1191.00 Graduate Teaching Assistants
21-1091.00 Health Educators
25-1125.00 History Teachers, Postsecondary
25-9031.00 Instructional Coordinators
23-1023.00 Judges, Magistrate Judges, and Magistrates**
25-1022.00 Mathematical Science Teachers, Postsecondary**

25-1072.00 Nursing Instructors and Teachers, Postsecondary
29-9011.00 Occupational Health and Safety Specialists
25-1065.00 Political Science Teachers, Postsecondary
25-1066.00 Psychology Teachers, Postsecondary
25-1067.00 Sociology Teachers, Postsecondary

** The occupation was assigned to the group based on its second highest interest area.
*** The occupation was assigned to the group based on its third highest interest area.

ENTERPRISING OCCUPATIONS

ENTERPRISING — JOB ZONE 1 (Little or No Preparation Needed)

39-6011.00 Baggage Porters and Bellhops
33-3011.00 Bailiffs**
35-3011.00 Bartenders
41-2011.00 Cashiers**
35-2015.00 Cooks, Short Order**
43-4041.01 Credit Authorizers**
41-9011.00 Demonstrators and Product Promoters
41-9091.00 Door-To-Door Sales Workers, News and Street Vendors, and Related Workers
53-3031.00 Driver/Sales Workers
45-3011.00 Fishers and Related Fishing Workers**
39-3093.00 Locker Room, Coat room, and Dressing Room Attendants**
39-5092.00 Manicurists and Pedicurists
41-9012.00 Models**
43-4171.00 Receptionists and Information Clerks**
33-9032.00 Security Guards**
53-6031.00 Service Station Attendants**
41-9041.00 Telemarketers
39-6021.00 Tour Guides and Escorts**
39-6032.00 Transportation Attendants, Except Flight Attendants and Baggage Porters
35-3031.00 Waiters and Waitresses**

ENTERPRISING — JOB ZONE 2 (Some Preparation Needed)

43-3011.00 Bill and Account Collectors**
39-6031.00 Flight Attendants
39-3012.00 Gaming and Sports Book Writers and Runners
39-3011.00 Gaming Dealers
43-4081.00 Hotel, Motel, and Resort Desk Clerks**
43-4161.00 Human Resources Assistants, Except Payroll and Timekeeping**
43-4131.00 Loan Interviewers and Clerks**
41-2022.00 Parts Salespersons
33-9021.00 Private Detectives and Investigators
43-5061.00 Production, Planning, and Expediting Clerks**
41-9022.00 Real Estate Sales Agents
41-2031.00 Retail Salespersons
41-4011.01 Sales Representatives, Agricultural
41-4011.03 Sales Representatives, Electrical/Electronic
41-4011.04 Sales Representatives, Mechanical Equipment and Supplies
41-4012.00 Sales Representatives, Wholesale and Manufacturing, Except Technical and Scientific Products

13-2082.00 Tax Preparers**
33-3052.00 Transit and Railroad Police
41-3041.00 Travel Agents
39-6022.00 Travel Guides

ENTERPRISING — JOB ZONE 3 (Medium Preparation Needed)

41-3011.00 Advertising Sales Agents
13-1011.00 Agents and Business Managers of Artists, Performers, and Athletes
27-2021.00 Athletes and Sports Competitors
45-1011.01 First-Line Supervisors and Manager/Supervisors - Agricultural Crop Workers
47-1011.02 First-Line Supervisors and Manager/Supervisors - Extractive Workers
43-1011.02 First-Line Supervisors, Administrative Support
43-1011.01 First-Line Supervisors, Customer Service
39-1021.00 First-Line Supervisors/Managers of Personal Service Workers
51-1011.00 First-Line Supervisors/Managers of Production and Operating Workers
53-1031.00 First-Line Supervisors/Managers of Transportation and Material-Moving Machine and Vehicle Operators
39-5012.00 Hairdressers, Hairstylists, and Cosmetologists
35-9031.00 Hosts and Hostesses, Restaurant, Lounge, and Coffee Shop
13-1031.02 Insurance Adjusters, Examiners, and Investigators
41-3021.00 Insurance Sales Agents
37-1011.02 Janitorial Supervisors
11-9081.00 Lodging Managers
13-1071.02 Personnel Recruiters
41-3031.02 Sales Agents, Financial Services
41-4011.02 Sales Representatives, Chemical and Pharmaceutical
41-4011.05 Sales Representatives, Medical

** The occupation was assigned to the group based on its second highest interest area.
*** The occupation was assigned to the group based on its third highest interest area.

ENTERPRISING — JOB ZONE 4 (Considerable Preparation Needed)

13-2021.02 Appraisers, Real Estate
35-1011.00 Chefs and Head Cooks
11-3031.02 Financial Managers, Branch or Department

183

47-1011.01 First-Line Supervisors and Manager/Supervisors - Construction Trades Workers
49-1011.00 First-Line Supervisors/Managers of Mechanics, Installers, and Repairers
11-9051.00 Food Service Managers
11-1011.01 Government Service Executives
37-1011.01 Housekeeping Supervisors
11-3040.00 Human Resources Managers
17-2112.00 Industrial Engineers
13-2071.00 Loan Counselors
13-1111.00 Management Analysts
11-9111.00 Medical and Health Services Managers
29-2081.00 Opticians, Dispensing
23-2011.00 Paralegals and Legal Assistants
33-3021.01 Police Detectives
27-3031.00 Public Relations Specialists
41-3031.01 Sales Agents, Securities and Commodities
11-2022.00 Sales Managers
53-5021.01 Ship and Boat Captains

ENTERPRISING — JOB ZONE 5 (Extensive Preparation Needed)

23-1021.00 Administrative Law Judges, Adjudicators, and Hearing Officers

23-1022.00 Arbitrators, Mediators, and Conciliators
27-2022.00 Coaches and Scouts
11-3021.00 Computer and Information Systems Managers
21-2021.00 Directors, Religious Activities and Education**
19-3011.00 Economists**
11-9033.00 Education Administrators, Postsecondary
11-9041.00 Engineering Managers
33-1021.02 Forest Fire Fighting and Prevention Supervisors**
19-3032.00 Industrial-Organizational Psychologists**
23-1023.00 Judges, Magistrate Judges, and Magistrates
23-1011.00 Lawyers
11-9121.00 Natural Sciences Managers**
29-9011.00 Occupational Health and Safety Specialists**
53-5021.03 Pilots, Ship**
11-1011.02 Private Sector Executives
27-2012.03 Program Directors
41-9031.00 Sales Engineers
53-5031.00 Ship Engineers**
11-3031.01 Treasurers, Controllers, and Chief Financial Officers

** The occupation was assigned to the group based on its second highest interest area.
*** The occupation was assigned to the group based on its third highest interest area.

CONVENTIONAL OCCUPATIONS

CONVENTIONAL — JOB ZONE 1 (Little or No Preparation Needed)

43-3021.03 Billing, Posting, and Calculating Machine Operators
41-2011.00 Cashiers
43-2021.02 Central Office Operators
41-2021.00 Counter and Rental Clerks
43-4041.02 Credit Checkers
43-2021.01 Directory Assistance Operators
43-9071.01 Duplicating Machine Operators
43-4071.00 File Clerks
43-4111.00 Interviewers, Except Eligibility and Loan
43-4121.00 Library Assistants, Clerical
43-9051.02 Mail Clerks, Except Mail Machine Operators and Postal Service
43-5081.02 Marking Clerks
43-5041.00 Meter Readers, Utilities
43-9061.00 Office Clerks, General
33-3041.00 Parking Enforcement Workers
43-5052.00 Postal Service Mail Carriers
43-3061.00 Procurement Clerks
43-4171.00 Receptionists and Information Clerks
43-5071.00 Shipping, Receiving, and Traffic Clerks
43-2011.00 Switchboard Operators, Including Answering Service

CONVENTIONAL — JOB ZONE 2 (Some Preparation Needed)

43-3011.00 Bill and Account Collectors
43-3031.00 Bookkeeping, Accounting, and Auditing Clerks
43-5011.00 Cargo and Freight Agents
43-4061.01 Claims Takers, Unemployment Benefits
43-4051.02 Customer Service Representatives, Utilities
33-2021.01 Fire Inspectors

53-6051.06 Freight Inspectors
43-4081.00 Hotel, Motel, and Resort Desk Clerks
43-9041.01 Insurance Claims Clerks
25-4031.00 Library Technicians
43-4031.02 Municipal Clerks
43-3051.00 Payroll and Timekeeping Clerks
29-2052.00 Pharmacy Technicians
43-5051.00 Postal Service Clerks
43-4181.02 Reservation and Transportation Ticket Agents
43-6014.00 Secretaries, Except Legal, Medical, and Executive
43-5081.03 Stock Clerks- Stockroom, Warehouse, or Storage Yard
13-2082.00 Tax Preparers
43-3071.00 Tellers
23-2093.01 Title Searchers

CONVENTIONAL — JOB ZONE 3 (Medium Preparation Needed)

49-2011.01 Automatic Teller Machine Servicers**
19-4061.01 City Planning Aides
43-9011.00 Computer Operators
47-4011.00 Construction and Building Inspectors
43-4031.01 Court Clerks
51-9061.04 Electrical and Electronic Inspectors and Testers**
41-1012.00 First- Line Supervisors/Managers of Non-Retail Sales Workers**
53-1021.00 First-Line Supervisors/Managers of Helpers, Laborers, and Material Movers, Hand**
11-9071.00 Gaming Managers**
39-1011.00 Gaming Supervisors**
33-3021.05 Immigration and Customs Inspectors
43-6012.00 Legal Secretaries
13-1041.02 Licensing Examiners and Inspectors
17-3031.02 Mapping Technicians

51-9061.01 Materials Inspectors**
29-2071.00 Medical Records and Health Information Technicians
43-6013.00 Medical Secretaries
33-3021.02 Police Identification and Records Officers
23-2093.02 Title Examiners and Abstractors
13-1022.00 Wholesale and Retail Buyers, Except Farm Products**

CONVENTIONAL — JOB ZONE 4 (Considerable Preparation Needed)

13-2011.01 Accountants
11-3011.00 Administrative Services Managers**
53-2021.00 Air Traffic Controllers
13-2021.01 Assessors
27-4011.00 Audio and Video Equipment Technicians
25-9011.00 Audio-Visual Collections Specialists
13-2011.02 Auditors
13-2031.00 Budget Analysts
17-1021.00 Cartographers and Photogrammetrists
13-1031.01 Claims Examiners, Property and Casualty Insurance
13-1051.00 Cost Estimators
13-2041.00 Credit Analysts
17-3012.02 Electrical Drafters
43-6011.00 Executive Secretaries and Administrative Assistants
11-3051.00 Industrial Production Managers**
13-1032.00 Insurance Appraisers, Auto Damage
13-2053.00 Insurance Underwriters

29-1051.00 Pharmacists**
15-2041.00 Statisticians**
13-2081.00 Tax Examiners, Collectors, and Revenue Agents

CONVENTIONAL — JOB ZONE 5 (Extensive Preparation Needed)

15-2011.00 Actuaries
25-4011.00 Archivists**
19-2011.00 Astronomers***
11-3021.00 Computer and Information Systems Managers**
25-1021.00 Computer Science Teachers, Postsecondary**
51-5022.08 Dot Etchers**
19-3011.00 Economists***
51-5022.10 Electrotypers and Stereotypers**
13-2051.00 Financial Analysts**
51-5021.00 Job Printers**
23-1011.00 Lawyers**
53-6051.03 Marine Cargo Inspectors
25-1022.00 Mathematical Science Teachers, Postsecondary***
15-2021.00 Mathematicians**
51-5023.02 Offset Lithographic Press Setters and Set-Up Operators**
19-2012.00 Physicists***
51-5022.11 Plate Finishers**
11-1011.02 Private Sector Executives**
53-5031.00 Ship Engineers***
11-3031.01 Treasurers, Controllers, and Chief Financial Officers**

Appendix B:

Related Web sites

There are literally hundreds of websites that relate to career development and planning. Those sites are of varying quality and purpose. This chapter provides descriptions of several specially selected websites that can support your career development efforts as they apply to helping students and clients use and understand their interests.

In this section, we have provided you summaries of sites that allow you to download interest inventories and use them with your students or clients. There are sites that quickly and easily link an individual's interest areas to hobbies, occupations, and educational programs. Further, there are sites that provide the latest information on the occupational and job outlook for various occupations.

Each of the websites has been visited and reviewed for accuracy and utility. The sites listed in this section were selected because the information is generally solid, current, and high quality. They provide good information for use by you or your students or clients.

As of the date of this publication all the site addresses or URLs were active and accurate. However, it is not unusual for sites to change their address periodically. Should this happen, just enter the name of the site into a search engine such as Google or Yahoo! in order to find the current URL.

Use of these web sites will surely supplement your career development library of resources and assist your students and clients in understanding how interests play a role in career exploration and decision.

The web sites include:

- America's Job Bank
- Bureau of Labor Statistics
- Career and Technical Education—Natonal Dissemination Center, National Research Center
- Career Info Net
- Career Information for Kids
- Career One Stop
- Career Voyages
- Creating a Graph
- Finding a Major or Career—MU Career Center Interest Games
- MBNA Career Services Center
- New York Career Zone
- Occupational Outlook Handbook
- O*NET Center
- The ASVAB Program
- Today's Military
- University of California, Berkeley Health Services
- Workforce USA

America's Job Bank

http://www.ajb.org/

As of this writing there are more than 1.3 million jobs listed in the job bank. They can be accessed by category and by state. The site has other useful resources and links. You can post a resume and learn how to develop a cover letter to a prospective employer.

Bureau of Labor Statistics

http://www.bls.gov

This site offers a wealth of information and statistics about various occupations and industries. Various publications, such as the *Occupational Outlook Quarterly*, are also available from this site. Up-to-date information on the U.S. economy is provided.

Career and Technical Education – National Dissemination Center, National Research Center

http://www.nccte.org/about/who.asphttp://www.nccte.org/index.asp

This site has useful papers and presentations on career and technical education. It is sponsored by a consortium of several universities and represents some of this nation's premier providers of career and technical instructor, administrator, and counselor education. The Consortium uses the expertise of a National Advisory Council of leading experts and a number of internationally recognized consultants.

Career Info Net

http://www.acinet.org/acinet/default.asp

This site is especially good for finding state labor market information, employers, and wage and employment trends. It has an extensive career resource library that you will find useful.

Career Information for Kids

http://www.bls.gov/k12/html/edu_over.htm

This website focuses on occupations in the areas of music/arts, math, science, social studies, PE/outdoors, and reading. After selecting one of the areas, information is provided on what people in various related occupations do, what the education and training needs are, etc. For example, for students interested in social studies, the occupations of lawyer, clergy, police officer, politician, real estate agent, and urban planner are described. The site contains information about occupations that kids would be attracted to such as rock star and pilot. The realities of the occupation are described. A teacher's site provides more extensive information about the occupations and it can be found at http://www.bls.gov/k12/html/edu_tch.htm.

Career One Stop

http://www.careeronestop.org/CareerTools/CareerTools.asp

This site offers licensing and certification information, employer information, scholarship search data, financial aid information, scholarship searches, and other career resources. Access to 450 career videos can be viewed from this site. Click on the Career Tools section for information on a vast array of resources available to persons exploring careers and searching for jobs.

Career Voyages

http://www.careervoyages.gov/

The site is co-sponsored by the U.S. Department of Labor and the U.S. Department of Education. This website offers current information on various industries and the jobs that have the best opportunities. Projections of job openings by state are a helpful part of this site. Job-hunting tips and information on education and training are provided.

Creating a Graph

http://nces.ed.gov/nceskids/graphing/

Several activities in this book suggest that students create a graph showing various relationships between interests and other factors. This site helps students understand the various types of graphs and how to create one.

Finding a Major or Career—MU Career Center Interests Games

http://career.missouri.edu/modules.php?name=News&file=article&sid=146

On this site individuals can select the most applicable Holland interest code and they will be directed to personality traits, abilities, hobbies, and school programs and careers. It is quick and easy to use and is applicable to individuals regardless of the education level to which a person aspires. It is not dependent on having an interest in the university that sponsors this site.

MBNA Career Services Center

http://www.udel.edu/CSC/mrk.html

This site helps an individual link a university major to a career path through the provision of online career resources kits. For example, if a person selects biology as the major area of study, the site will provide a description of the major, sample job titles, related careers where knowledge of biology is important for someone with an undergraduate degree in that areaand also for those with advanced degrees, and more. Typical employers are listed, such as government, book publishers, pharmaceutical companies, etc. A listing of related websites for further information is also listed.

New York Career Zone

http://www.nycareerzone.org/

Click on "Assess Yourself." This site asks individuals to select three of the six Holland interest areas starting with the most important one. After the selections are made, the site will show a list of various occupations that relate to that interest code combination. Many of the occupations have career videos that provide a capsule overview of the work in that occupation. These videos were prepared under the sponsorship of the U.S. Department of Labor. The site helps individuals understand that generally, people and occupations are made up of more than one interest area.

Occupational Outlook Handbook

http://www.bls.gov/oco/

This is the most comprehensive resource describing various occupations, what people do in those occupations, the amount of education and training needed, working conditions, earnings, and the outlook for jobs in these occupations. The occupations are listed according to the following categories: Management, Business, and Financial, Professional and Related, Service, Sales, Office and Administrative Support, Farming and Related, Construction, Installation and Related, Production, Transportation, and Job Opportunities in the Armed Forces.

O*NET Center

http://online.onetcenter.org

Produced by the U.S. Department of Labor, this site provides an enormous amount of information on occupations, focused on the O*NET occupations. Additionally, available for download are three solid career development tools, the Interest Profiler, the Work Importance Profiler, and the Ability Profiler. Additional publications on assessment issues and the use of assessment in the workplace are available from this site. The information is free.

The ASVAB Program

http://www.asvabprogram.com

The site describes the ASVAB Career Exploration Program and its components. The interests section offers some explanatory information about the RIASEC interest codes. In the Career Planning Tools section, there is a career planning guide and a course planning guide that could be useful to students.

Today's Military

http://www.todaysmilitary.com

This site provides extensive information about jobs in the military, both enlisted and officer. A very comprehensive site. Information can be found on military life in general, benefits, education and training, compensation, etc.

University of California, Berkeley Health Services

http://uhs.berkeley.edu/Students/CareerLibrary/links/assess.shtml

This website is useful because it provides a concise overview of the six RIASEC areas.

Workforce USA

http://www.workforceusa.net/home/index.cfm

workforceUSA.net is a collaboration among workforce development organizations and professionals. The site was developed to help people trying to find useful tools and materials for a wide variety of workforce development projects. The financial support for the project has come from the U.S. Department of Labor-Employment and Training Administration, the Ford Foundation, and the Rockefeller Foundation. The site has information on training and education, program management, assessment, and other important career development components.

About the Author

Dr. Janet Wall is President of her own consulting company, Sage Solutions. She specializes in assessment and career development. During her career, she led the development of the ASVAB Career Exploration Program for the U.S. Department of Defense, to include the development of the Interest Finder and consulted for the U.S. Department of Labor during the development of their Interest Profiler. She presents, trains, and writes on the subjects of assessment, career development, use of technology in assessment, and interests. She is past President of the Association for Assessment in Counseling and Education and is co-editor of *Measuring Up: Assessment Issues for Teachers, Counselors, and Administrators*, also published by PRO-ED Inc. Contact Janet at sagesolutions@earthlink.net.